THE BOWED TENDON BOOK

TOM IVERS

THE RUSSELL MEERDINK COMPANY, LTD.
1555 SOUTH PARK AVENUE
NEENAH, WI 54956
(800) 635-6499
(920) 725-0955 WORLDWIDE
WWW.HORSEINFO.COM

Library of Congress Cataloging-in-Publication Data

Ivers, Tom
    The Bowed Tendon Book / by Tom Ivers
    Includes index.
    1. Bowed tendon.   1. Title.
SF959.B65194   1993
636. 1'0897474 – dc20   93-29819
                                          CIP

ISBN 0-929346-25-4 $24.95   First printing 1994

       0-929346-81-5   Second printing 2006
       9780929346816

Printed in the United States of America

Acknowledgments

I would like to thank Jan and Russ Meerdink for their invaluable help with this book, from its origin through to completion. Sara Schaefer was a patient editor and contributed solid thought and organization in making the book readable despite its technical content. Dr. Lowell Wickman deserves thanks for helping to translate veterinary shorthand into understandable language. And Graphic Artist Judy Hanson did a fine job with complex artistic concepts.

The Russell Meerdink Company publishing team has been both inspirational and extremely cooperative in both book ventures we've done together. Professionals.

For Erin

Contents

Introduction

Sport and injury are close companions. Seldom does an athlete make it through even a brief career without multiple injuries, and equine athletes are no exception. Minor injury is to be expected frequently in the athletic horse and most high-performance horses will encounter one or another of the more serious kind: fracture, degenerative joint disease, and serious soft tissue injuries in the tendons and suspensories. If you want to survive in the business of dealing with athletic horses, you must learn to deal with, or prevent, these more serious injuries.

Everybody makes mistakes, hundreds or thousands of them in a lifetime, and some are quite painful to live through. There is a peculiar shock of devastation that comes with the first discovery of a hot, swollen tendon on a fit, bright-eyed, forever willing equine athlete that you've worked with for months or years. In some animals it means the abrupt end of a promising career. In others, it is a nagging, recurring problem that severely limits athletic potential. But, properly handled and rehabilitated, most horses suffering bowed tendons can become fine athletes participating in less demanding sports than the one in which they were originally injured. There are many ex-racehorses, for example, that live long, useful lives as show horses, polo ponies, endurance and event animals after having bowed a tendon during all-out competition.

Rarely, though, does the bowed horse come back for more of the same kind of punishment that injured its tendon in the first place. A good portion of this book is devoted to examining the causes of bows with an eye toward prevention, and intervention in the case of an oncoming bow. It is a far more enjoyable and rewarding task to take steps to avoid a bow than to rehabilitate one.

Whatever your situation, I hope this book enables you to enjoy your equine friend, preserve your investment, and happily pursue your sport. I hope it arms you with information, encourages you to think far ahead, and augments your horsemanship. We are like gods to our horses, and with that power comes the responsibility to provide the best and kindest environment deliverable by mere humans.

Perhaps this book will offer some hope when you need it, some knowledge that you can instantly put to work. Some courage to meet the challenge. That's what books are for, and why I write them. I'll give you my best, and you'll have to take it from there. So stand up, brush the dust off your butt, and get to work!

Tom Ivers
Vevay, Indiana
1993

Disclaimer

While the techniques and methods described in this book are drawn from the author's extensive experience in the business of horse racing, this book is not all inclusive on the subject matter and may not apply in all circumstances. This book is not intended to offer veterinary advice. The reader should consult with professional advisors such as veterinarians and other competent authorities to determine whether the subject matter is appropriate for use in a specific instance. Neither the author nor the publisher assume any liability or make any guarantees of any nature for any outcome resulting from use of the procedures and techniques described herein.

Chapter 1: The Words of an Expert

We bow and cripple thousands of racehorses each year, starting them too young and racing them without adequate preparation. Although the other performance sports bow horses at a lower frequency, the same problems exist.

Some people call that "unavoidable" or "the breaks of the game." I call it idiocy, and have made many enemies saying so. Most of these people can't read, but some do, and they tell their buddies that I'm saying nasty things about them, calling them lunatics, morons, what have you. What they never seem to read in my books is the places where I call myself a moron. Let me do that right now, so you'll know I'm just as human as you are. I've been just as much a moron as anyone I've ever met in the horse business. Just as much a coward. Just as lazy. Just as greedy.

Yes, I've crippled horses. I've been in the horse racing game for too many years to try to remember them all, but I remember some of them way too well. Well enough that it makes a hard fist in my gut when I think back - because I now know how I've crippled most of them. I know how my readers have crippled a couple thousand more. I know how you're most likely to cripple one of your horses. So I try to think forward instead. I try to make up for my stupidity by learning as much as I can from my mistakes. I read everything about exercise, equine and human, that I can get my hands on. I read about biomechanics, muscle biochemistry, anatomy, sportsmedicine - everything. I'm in contact with hundreds of trainers and owners, and I live through their experiences with them. We all record everything we do with horses, all the little things like hoof angles, toe lengths, heartrate responses, workout protocols and times - everything we can write down. Then we go back and look closely at the facts concerning a horse that has been injured, trying to determine precisely what went wrong so that we can avoid making the same stupid mistake a second time. After about 3,000 mistakes, you become an "expert".

And that's what qualifies me to be your expert on

bowed tendons. Check out the next few pages and see if you think I know what I'm talking about.

A Word of Hope

One very good reason for your purchase of this book may be that you have a horse already bowed, standing there in the stall with his big brown eyes, wondering what all the fuss is about. Horses don't understand the tragedy of the bow - it's just another pain to get over and go on with life. But we know how devastating and long-term a ruptured tendon can be. We're discouraged before we even begin the healing process. And those of us working with racehorses are most easily discouraged, probably because we've seen hundreds of bowed horses returned to competition too early, only to bow again, worse the second time. Bows scare us to death.

I've witnessed miracles where a bowed racehorse was back winning, some in as little as 120 days. It can be done, and it has been done thousands of times. But more often, a bow is a career-ending tragedy.

There is certainly life for a racehorse after a bow, and many times that life includes racing and winning. Once-bowed Thoroughbreds and Quarter Horses often make very suitable hunters, polo ponies, dressage horses, endurance athletes, pleasure horses, barrel racers, reining horses, eventers, and rodeo animals - you name it and the new sport is almost always easier on the tendons than flat racing. Some stars over fences like Idle Dice, Aldaniti, Cure the Blues and Snowbound were once bowed tendon victims.

So, while this book pulls no punches in trying to persuade you to avoid bowing a horse in the first place, just keep in mind that a large part of this book is devoted to bringing the animal back to full capacity. It will require a lot of time and patient rehabilitative exercise, but a bowed tendon can heal completely.

You Can Make A Difference

As you read through this book, you're going to find that there is more to handling bowed tendons than the old routine of firing, blistering, and throwing the horse out in a field for a year. There's a lot you can do - first, by not firing or blistering. Actually, even before the bow becomes apparent, if you've been monitoring your horse's legs closely, you'll see the signs of oncoming problems. Catching a bow early, before severe damage takes place, is the very best opportunity you have to save your horse's athletic career.

Once you're dealing with a bow, proper care and gradual rehabilitation through a progressively loaded exercise program will ensure a stronger more viable tendon when you eventually go back to work. And if you can determine the cause of the bow, you'll be way ahead of the assembly-line trainers who just don't care. They'll be creating more problems for their horses while you'll be avoiding them.

Chin up! If your horse has a bow, this is no time to quit on him. Let's take a hard look at the problem. Read on!

Chapter 2: The Ball On The Chain

Horses walk, trot and gallop on the tips of their middle fingers - their middle fingernails, to be precise. The horse's "knee" is the equivalent of the human wrist. The tendons of the foreleg make their way down the back of the leg from all the way up at their connections to the forearm muscles. The flexor tendons flex or pull the hoof and leg up under the horse's body. The extensor tendons extend or straighten, drawing the hoof and leg forward. They're like the strings that control the limbs of a puppet. They not only control the motion of the parts of the leg, but they're responsible for locking the links of chain (bones) into proper position as the hoof hits the ground.

So between the hoof and the muscles that control it is a whale of a distance, and there's not a lot of control. Instead of precision placement, the hoof flies through the air like a ball on a chain, expecting the links of that chain to eventually snap into place and hold firm as the foot hits the ground. There's a lot that can go wrong with that chain.

The hoof wobbles as it's flying through the air. If it comes down too soon, in the middle of a wobble, then it can hit toe first and you get a buckling effect, and probably some injuries to bones all up and down the leg. If the hoof hits heel first in the middle of a wobble, then the knee will tend to bend backwards and crush a few bones - usually the middle carpal bone goes first. The bones of the knee are like a packet of chicklets that splay apart when the knee is bent and then all snap together, hopefully in their proper positions, when the leg straightens. If any of them is out of place at that moment, the cartilage around the bones is crushed and there is an instant of searing pain that triggers the rest of the chain to buckle, just like your leg would buckle if you started to sprain your ankle. The horse will stumble or fall down.

The flexor tendons are also responsible for taking up a lot of the initial shock of impact by stretching like very stout rubber bands. Not much play in them, but enough to give the bones, and the cartilage of their joints, a break. In a galloping horse, the lead foreleg eventually takes the entire weight of the horse for a fraction of a second (about .11 of a second, to be exact) as the body rolls over the leg. During this short period of time, the tendons are stretched to the max, and many times, beyond their capacity to stretch. Instead of snapping like rubber bands, they just tear. Sometimes it's a small tear and sometimes most of the tendon pulls apart - it all depends on the forces being applied to the tendon versus the strength of the tendon at that particular instant.

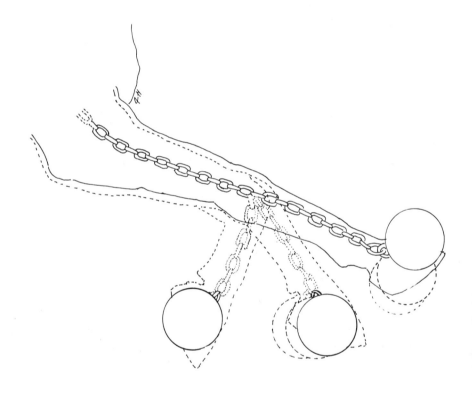

The hoof is a long way from the muscles which control it. As a result, the hoof flies through the air like a ball on a chain. *(Illustration by Judy Hanson)*

Of course, there are other structures helping the tendons to do their jobs. The muscles of the forearm can absorb some stretch, and they do, until they become fatigued. When they're fatigued, the muscles just relax, let go, and the fetlock droops, throwing a whole lot more work onto the flexor tendons. There are ligaments which connect bones to bones (tendons connect muscles to bones) that help stabilize the leg. Ligaments are shorter and stiffer than tendons - they help to hold those chicklets in the knee together and will wrap around other joints, keeping them tight and allowing very little motion except in the right direction. There's not much stretch available in ligaments, but they do help to absorb some of the shock and other forces (torque, shear, bending, twisting). It's probably the length of the flexor tendons that makes them far more susceptible to injury than most ligaments of the foreleg.

Now, the foreleg is supposed to curl up and travel forward, then straighten out, locking all the links of the chain, then begin to move backward, before the hoof hits the ground. This eliminates more than a thousand pounds of extra concussion upon impact. But, if the leg is slow to travel through its cycle, then it will just be straightening out when the hoof hits the ground. This occurs with fatigue, and Go For Wand's cataclysmic breakdown in the 1990 Breeder's Cup is a good example of what happens under these conditions.

Go For Wand was a wonderful race mare with a beautiful, effortless stride. And that stride was perfectly evident as she came out of the gate and flowed down the straightaway in her final race. But the horses in the Breeder's Cup are the best in the world and Go For Wand had her work cut out for her. Coming out of the final turn for home, she made a very nice move, but could not break contact with the competition - they were right with her. Over the last 16th of a mile, the strides of all the lead horses noticeably shortened, and their heads bobbed as they tried to throw their fatigued forelegs forward, passing some of that work to the neck muscles. For several strides in a row, Go For Wand didn't have time to develop a rearward swing of her foreleg before it hit the ground. Then the extra concussion overwhelmed her ankle and it snapped.

You can see that the equine foreleg is a mechanical

system that is just barely under control at any point in time. If anything goes wrong in the stride, then instantly 5,000 to 12,000 pounds of force can be applied to any part of the leg, and bones snap, ligaments pull away from their attachments, cartilage is crushed, and tendons tear. Foreleg injuries are very easy to accomplish in the equine athlete.

The good news is that there are measures we can take to avoid these injuries. All of the structures of the foreleg can be gradually strengthened with the right kind of progressively loaded exercise. That's because the horse is a living organism, and living things adapt to the stresses they encounter in life. In the athlete, we call this adaptation increased fitness, or conditioning. What it means is that, after a few months of training, the athlete can do more strenuous work safely than he could when he first went into training. And conditioning can go on almost forever - 15 year-old horses are capable of benefiting from exercise, and older horses probably will too.

Training makes the action of the ball on the end of the chain more accurate with each stride. There is neuromuscular coordination developing throughout the conditioning process that makes mistakes in hoof placement less likely. Sometimes we call this agility, sometimes stride efficiency. Whatever we call it, it means that all the structures of the leg take less punishment.

Training and conditioning must be broken down into many stages and small steps. Every time we change what it is we want the equine athlete to do - go faster, jump higher, make sharper turns, stop more quickly - the structural systems have to be given a chance to adapt to the new stresses. And structural organs, like tendons, ligaments, bone and cartilage, are much slower to adapt than are the muscles. It is quite easy, then, to build young horses that can outrun their legs. If we rush the process, then the wheels fall off.

Chapter 3: What Is a Bowed Tendon?

In the simplest terms, a bowed tendon is a ruptured tendon. That is, there are torn or broken fibers in the tendon itself. The term "bow" is taken from the appearance of a ruptured superficial digital flexor tendon - the curving outward of the swollen tendon tissue. But, of course, simple terms never really describe complex problems and "bowed tendon" can refer, mistakenly or not, to a variety of conditions involving the stay apparatus of the horse: tendinitis, ruptured deep or superficial flexor tendons, tenosynovitis, check ligament injury, carpal channel injury, sesamoiditis, injured suspensory ligaments - even a skin fungus or an allergic reaction to a topical application can appear to be a "bow."

Simply eyeballing and palpating a horse's leg can neither tell you whether you have a torn tendon, nor can it tell you when that tendon has healed. That's why the very first step you must take when dealing with what may be a bow is to get a proper and complete diagnosis. Luckily, with the advent of the ultrasound sector scanner, veterinarians are able to see into soft tissue, much in the way that X-rays look into bones, and determine exactly which tissues are damaged and the extent of that damage.

For our purposes in this book, we're going to be talking essentially about superficial digital flexor tendon injuries and, to a lesser extent, about deep digital flexor tendon injuries. But other organs, notably the check ligaments, the sesamoids, the suspensory ligaments, and even the splint bones, can influence the health of the flexor tendons. So, when talking about bowed tendons, even though we're primarily concerned with the rupture of the superficial digital flexor tendon, it is best to understand how the various parts of the leg of the horse are intended to work together - and how things go wrong.

Tendons connect muscles to bone while ligaments connect bone to bone. The structures of tendons and ligaments are similar, in that they are made up principally of bundles of collagen fibers arranged in-line with the direction of stretch, that is, end-to-end as opposed to across the tendon or ligament. (Collagen is a type of tough protein found in all the hard and semi-hard structures of the body, from bones and cartilage to tendons, ligaments and fascia. Collagen fibers look a lot like stringy roast beef.) But tendons also have some properties of muscles. They contain some contracting muscle cells for one thing, and they have more blood vessels within. In general, tendons are "stretchier" than ligaments. They tend to heal faster and more completely than ligaments - but they're more readily injured.

Take a look at Figure 1. Note that the superficial digital flexor tendon originates from, and is named after, the superficial digital flexor muscle. Similarly, the deep digital flexor tendon originates from the deep digital flexor muscle. The word "flexor" means that the muscle and tendon act to bend back or flex the leg. The point in the stride where the leg folds back under the horse is accomplished by the flexor muscles and flexor tendons. "Extensor," as the name implies, acts to straighten or extend a joint. The leg is pulled forward by the extensor muscles and extensor tendons. Most of the stresses imposed on the flexor tendons, though, occur when the hoof is on the ground and the knee joint is either straight or overextended (bent backwards).

The superficial digital flexor tendon, as it passes down the back of the cannon bone, lies closest to the skin, with the deep digital flexor tendon nestled just under it. The suspensory ligament, which is actually more of a tendon than a ligament in composition, lies closest to the bone. The superficial digital flexor tendon splits after passing over the sesamoids and inserts on the pastern bone. The deep digital flexor tendon passes through the sesamoid groove and extends all the way down over the navicular, into the hoof, to insert on the coffin bone. The suspensory ligament attaches at the sesamoids and splits into a pair of extensor ligaments that will wrap around to the front of the pastern.

What you have here is an elaborate cable and pulley system made of flesh and bone. It is designed to handle just so much of a load, even though the entire apparatus can be considerably strengthened through proper conditioning.

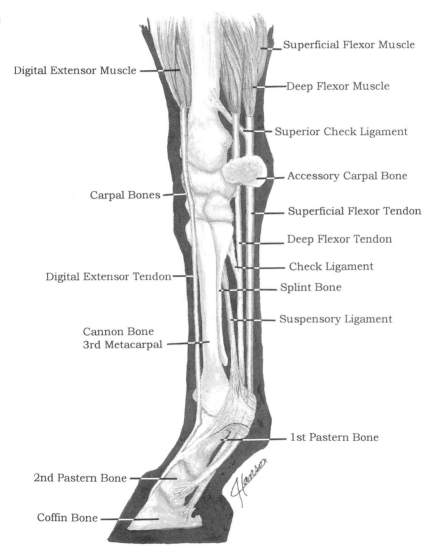

Digital Extensor Muscle

Superficial Flexor Muscle

Deep Flexor Muscle

Superior Check Ligament

Accessory Carpal Bone

Carpal Bones

Superficial Flexor Tendon

Deep Flexor Tendon

Check Ligament

Digital Extensor Tendon

Splint Bone

Suspensory Ligament

Cannon Bone
3rd Metacarpal

1st Pastern Bone

2nd Pastern Bone

Coffin Bone

Figure 1:   The flexor and extensor muscles and tendons of the foreleg.   *(Illustration by Judy Hanson)*

19

High, Middle and Low Bows Defined

In Figures 2 and 2A, the basic structures of the tendons are portrayed. They are surrounded by coverings that are thick within the knee capsule and thinner on down behind the cannon bone. Both types of coverings are commonly referred to as sheaths, but the thinner coating is properly called a paratenon. Within either coating, the tendon slides back and forth inside the sheath, depending on the forces applied to it.

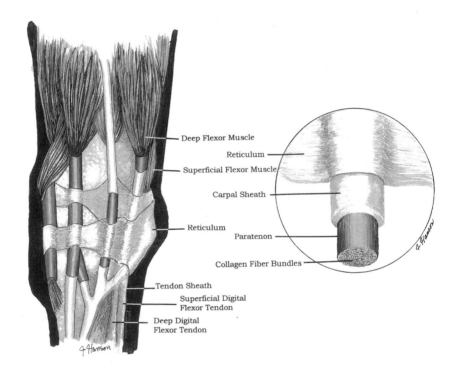

Figures 2 and 2A: An inside view of tendons as they pass through and continue on below the knee. The close-up on 2A shows the details of the tendon/paratenon/reticulatum/carpal sheath.

(Illustration by Judy Hanson)

A carpal sheath extends from the knee (carpus), wrapping around the flexor tendons to about the point where the check ligament inserts at the deep digital flexor tendon. The check ligament limits or "checks" the motion of the tendons. For example, if you suddenly raise the angles of the feet several degrees, once overstretched flexor tendons become somewhat slack and tend to exhibit a whiplike action when the hoof hits the ground that may irritate or tear the check ligament. Toe grabs accentuate the problem and likely cause check ligament damage all by themselves.

The superficial digital flexor tendon is most often torn at its thinnest point, its middle third. Thus "*middle bows*" are more likely to occur than "*high bows*" and "*low bows*."

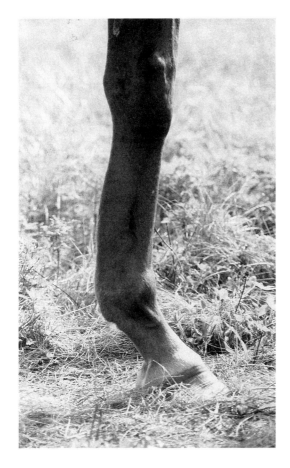

A classic, severe middle bow of the superficial digital flexor tendon. *(Photo by Suzie Oldham)*

Heat, pain and swelling in the first few inches below the knee is usually called a *high bow*, but this is not always an accurate description. This injury is often the result of insults to the check ligament.

The thinner paratenon surrounds the tendons as they pass down behind the cannon bone, until just above the fetlock joint, another sheath arises to protect the tendons as they enter the joint. At the fetlock, an annular ligament wraps around the entire joint, among other duties, keeping the tendons in place. It is in this area that the deep digital flexor tendon is more likely to become injured, commonly called a *low bow*. A low bow seldom involves just one structure, since a swollen deep digital flexor tendon will tend to squeeze the superficial digital flexor tendon against the relatively inflexible annular ligament, compromising its blood supply. Injury to the superficial digital flexor tendon in this location then becomes more likely.

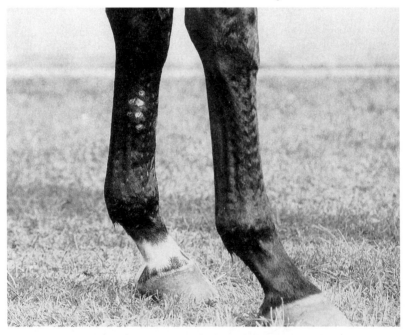

This horse has been pin fired with emphasis in the check ligament/splint area. Note the long, sloping pastern conformation of this horse - see **Chapter 5 for further discussion.** *(Photo by Suzie Oldham)*

A severe low bow. Injury and swelling in the deep digital flexor tendon could cause damage to the superficial digital flexor tendon. *(Photo by Suzie Oldham)*

All bones, ligaments, cartilage and tendons interact with one another in order to stabilize the action of the lower leg, and, depending on the kind of bad step the horse takes, any of them can be injured separately, without affecting the health of the other parts. However, if the trainer doesn't notice the problem early, and take steps to rehabilitate what might be a minor injury, then the next weakest link in the chain will sustain injury because the overload has been passed on. At some point, as one after another of the links fails, you'll have a catastrophe on your hands.

How Tendons Fail

The reason tendons rupture is that they become overstretched. A properly warmed-up superficial digital flexor tendon can stretch about 8% before it begins to fail and tear apart. Overextension (backward bending) of the knee occurs at the same time that the fetlock has dropped to its lowest point in the stride and the tendon is absorbing its highest stretching loads. There are times, in some horses, when the fetlock actually touches the ground (running down). A fetlock that travels too far toward the ground is said to be overdorsiflexed. A horse that experiences overextended knees and overdorsiflexed fetlocks often will eventually bow, unless his tendons are steel cables, or unless something else (i.e. sesamoids) breaks first. This condition arises most often as a result of fatigue, but it can be aggravated by deep going, uneven terrain, sudden changes in stress loads, low hoof angles and long toes, or simple missteps.

Overdorsiflexion at the knee. Multiple injuries, from the shoulder down to the hoof, result from this mechanical crisis. *(Photo courtesy of Equine Sports Graphics)*

Often the heat and swelling reaction to torn tendon tissue is delayed, sometimes for as long as three or four days. This leads the trainer or owner to conclude that the horse must have done something to himself in the stall, or that a leg bandage caused the injury. Don't believe it. More often than not, if you think back over several days, you'll remember the workout, or the event, that caused the bow.

Not only that, but the conditions that predisposed the horse to tear a tendon may have been in existence for a very long time, doing subtle damage all along. The latest scientific thoughts about bowed tendons are that a full blown bow (massive rupture) is the end state of a long series of insults, where some tendon tissue is damaged, then some more later, before the original damage can heal, until finally a whole section gives way.

Another theory is that compromised circulation, due to small tears in tissue and blood vessels, or due to bandages or boots that are too tight, leads to weakened areas that eventually rupture. A good case for this type of "compression" bow can be made for low bows of the deep flexor tendon that are caused when other injuries to the fetlock cause tissues to swell and constrict the deep flexor - it weakens and tears.

Still, it is the overstretching of the entire stay or suspensory apparatus that remains the immediate cause of most bows. In fact, almost all the soft tissue injuries of the foreleg and bone and cartilage injuries to the knee, ankle, and sesamoids, involve a drooping fetlock and overdorsiflexion of the joints. It can happen in an instant, landing from a jump, or it can happen slowly, as a horse nears the end of a long, hard race. Even more slowly: the horse gallops the same five miles he did yesterday, but this time over deep going, after a rain. And that tell-tale swelling the day after, the one you dismiss as a rap or minor strain, that's a bow.

Chapter 4: Sorting Out the Look-alikes

Now remember, just because you have filling in a lower leg, it doesn't mean you have a tendon problem. In young horses, there is sometimes a lack of elasticity in the blood vessels serving the lower leg. The veins, intended to carry blood toward the heart, have one-way valves that are supposed to close off backflow down into the legs. But bringing on the workload too fast with a young horse can result in an overwhelming of those too-pliable valves and a backwash will occur, setting up a condition called "stocking up".

Generally, there is not much heat associated with stocking up, because no repair is going on - unless you ignore the condition and keep on with the big workload. Then, the pressure of too much fluid in the lower leg will start to cause damage. Cutting the workload in half and eliminating any speed work will tend to allow the blood vessels to catch up. In a week or two, you're back to where you were, no harm done.

At the fetlock, other, similar, situations can arise that are of no consequence over the long term. For example, a sudden introduction to hard work or hard surfaces can cause the cartilage of the fetlock to exhibit some wear, and this will inflame the joint capsule - heat and swelling will appear. The outward sign of this activity is what we call "windpuffs." Again, if you back off the workload, the problem tends to resolve itself and you can eventually sneak back to where you were and beyond. Growthy, big-boned babies will drive you nuts with this kind of problem, but it will eventually stop recurring. Just take your time, giving the horse a break just as soon as he shows he needs it. Don't give up the work entirely, just baby the baby along.

The difference between wind puffs and suspensory or deep flexor problems is that wind puffs are generally cool, bubble-like pouches of fluid just above the fetlock and behind the suspensory and deep flexor. Suspensory and deep flexor injuries are harder swellings of tissue. Wind puffs are a reasonably innocent sign that some repair activity is taking place within the fetlock joint. They're not an injury of themselves, but they warn of disruptions within the joint.

Once in a while, a horse will have a blood vessel that wraps around the outside of the superficial flexor tendon, and this will scare you to death every time you look at the animal's legs. But the blood vessel will easily be recognized for what it is by simply pressing on it and discovering that it's a tube filled with liquid. The ones I've seen traveled diagonally across the back of the tendon, like a stripe on a barber pole.

On the other hand, if there is a condition that is actually putting stress on the tendons and they're complaining by getting hot and swelling, you've got to eliminate that cause immediately. Long toe, low heel shoeing is such a deadly circumstance that must be corrected. Deep, soggy going can be another. Too much fatigue-producing work is still another. You must know if you're dealing with a tendon problem and, if you are, you must determine what's causing it before going on. That's why veterinary diagnostics are your very best tool - assuming you have a vet who is equipped to perform complete diagnostics. If your vet doesn't have an ultrasound sector scanner, he's probably not a diagnostician. Find somebody else to take a scan if you're wondering whether or not you have an oncoming tendon problem. Then find somebody, usually a good shoer, who can do something about it. At this stage, the horse doesn't need medicine, he needs the elimination of the cause.

You've probably noticed that I've been talking about filling and swelling as two different problems and, in my mind, they are. Filling, or "stocking up," is a matter of the accumulation of fluids in the lower leg. The best theory for the cause of filling is that the blood vessels of a horse experiencing the sudden onset of increasingly difficult exercise are not ready for all the extra blood-borne traffic. Not elastic enough. So the little valves in the blood vessels that normally would prevent gravity from dragging fluids back down the leg to settle at the fetlock aren't as effective as they should be and some fluids leak back down the leg, causing the condition we know as stocking up or filling.

Swelling, on the other hand, is a localized reaction to an injury, usually accompanied by heat and pain.

If an ultrasound scan finds holes in your horse's tendon, you have a bow. If, instead, it finds fluid between the tendon and its sheath or paratenon, you have tendinitis - you're lucky. Tendinitis still represents damaged tissue, but not the kind that takes more than a year to heal. Tendinitis represents minor damage that will come along quickly if you eliminate the cause and ease up for a while, but keep the horse moving. Every strenuous exercise your horse experiences is going to do some microdamage to the tendons, and to virtually every other part of the body involved in the exercise. This is normal - it's what stimulates adaptation so that the animal can perform tougher and tougher exercises without becoming hurt.

You're going to notice tendinitis more quickly than an oncoming bow. Here there will be more widely distributed heat and thickness, usually low in the tendon, but sometimes from top to bottom - and down over the fetlock and behind the pastern. The horse will likely be slightly lame. **There will be no bump.** Exercise will tend to alleviate some of the swelling, but it will come back at night. However, tendinitis is another sign that something's not right with the workload, shoeing, or working surface and that, somewhere down the line, you're going to get a sudden introduction to equine disaster.

If you just stop with the horse with tendinitis, then adhesions can develop between the tendon and its outer covering. Then it will no longer glide properly through the sheath. If you go back to work after a layoff, those adhesions will break, and you'll have another episode of heat and soreness - more tendinitis. Sometimes you have to go through several cycles of this kind of repair before the whole area settles down. During this time, the exercise should be kept light, but regular.

It should be clear now how important an accurate diagnosis of a suspected tendon problem is. You have to know what you're dealing with. In one case, you can be dealing with something that has nothing to do with the tendons, something that will go away if you just ease off the work and take care of the horse for a few days or weeks. In another, you may have the beginnings of a bow, and if you kid yourself into thinking that you have no real problem, you're going to have a big disappointment soon. And, in the case of a torn tendon, or bow, you have to do everything you can to limit the damage and begin the repair process.

Chapter 5: Why Horses Bow

An unshod horse turned out in the paddock, grazing, galloping over uneven ground, taking turns at a 45 degree angle, slipping and sliding on mud and stumbling over rough terrain, screeching to a stop, never bows. Wild horses out on the prairie, running away from wolves and coyotes, over rocks, ravines, through creeks, and climbing mountains - almost never bow. We take a horse into a stall, shoe him, do as little work as possible and only on uniform, hole-free surfaces, and he bows, and his buddy bows, and the horse three doors on down the shedrow bows. And we blame the horse: "He bowed on me just when I had him ready to win." Folks, bowed tendons are man-made. The horse has nothing to do with it.

It doesn't take much of the wrong kind of stress to bow a tendon. I want to quote a paper[1] from a study done in England.

"The initial damage in natural tendon injury involves random stretching, slipping, and ultimately tearing of tendon fibres, followed by fibre lysis caused by release of degradative enzymes from damaged cells and from inflammatory cells attracted to the site of injury.

"Although there have been claims that previous degeneration is a necessary prerequisite for spontaneous tendon sprain to occur as a result of unusual loading, in larger horses it is quite clear that the digital flexor tendons are operating towards the limits of their mechanical strength even in controlled foot movement. Evans and Barbenel (1975) have shown that in most mammals the tensile strength of tendons lies in the range of 5 to 10 kg/mm2, while the cross-sectional area of the narrowest part of the SDFT of the average Thoroughbred horse is approximately 500 mm2. This would suggest that a maximum safe transmitted force would be between 25 and 50,000 N (1N= 1 kg/m/sec2). In a moderate sized Thoroughbred galloping at speed, whose weight is periodically taken on one leg, the upward and forward forces developed are in the order of 11,000N (Pratt and O'Connor 1978). Under these conditions

the forces acting through the superficial and deep flexor tendons and suspensory ligaments may be two to three times higher because of the fulcrum effect of the fetlock joint. This brings the potential forces being applied to the SDFT to well within the theoretical failure range. Incoordinated movement or slipping could well take the force transmitted through the tendon above the rupture level."

Under normal performance horse circumstances, we're always a few pounds of stretch away from a bow. You don't need a PhD in biomechanics to realize that when we start fooling around with shoeing and forced exercise, we'd better be damned careful about what we're asking the horse to face. And we'd better prepare him carefully, step by step, progressively bringing on the stretching and twisting forces that he'll have to face in competition.

We've discussed the anatomy of the flexor tendons and their relationship to the rest of the structures of the leg. We've talked about the physical changes that represent tendinitis and bowed tendons. And the cause: overstretching. Now let's see how we manage to create the circumstances under which normally tough, resilient, elastic structures like these can become compromised in a few seconds. Let me count the ways:

1. Fatigue

There are two kinds of fatigue in the performance horse: chemical and mechanical. And there are two forms of chemical fatigue: lactic acid fatigue and fatigue caused by fuel depletion. In both forms of chemical fatigue, the muscles of the forearm, and all the other propulsion and stabilization muscles of the body, lose their ability to contract and, instead, relax. When the muscles relax, the tendons must take up the slack, absorbing rapidly increasing forces as the fetlocks droop lower and lower toward the ground. Worse, the lowered fetlock overdorsiflexes the leg, the knee bends backward, and the toe refuses to break over at the end of the contact phase of the stride. This throws the gait into increasingly erratic motion and missteps begin to occur. Some fibers in the tendon pull apart with the first fatigued stride, weakening the tendon. With each new stride, the fetlock sinks further toward the ground. At this stage of fatigue, broken bones a la Go For Wand often occur. Considerable injury to the tendon is virtually guaranteed.

The drooping fetlock of the fatigued horse. Also known as "running down," this condition puts excess stress on all the organs of the lower leg.

(Photo by Louise Reinagel)

Prevention of chemical fatigue is a matter of developing a level of fitness appropriate to the demands you expect to make on the animal. Later we'll examine this in detail. Fuel depletion can be fought on two fronts, appropriate exercise combined with fully supportive nutrition. Again, in depth later.

Mechanical, or structural fatigue can be likened to what happens to a paper clip when you bend it back and forth over and over again. At some point, it breaks. Concussive stresses, especially those involved in jumping or running at maximum speed, sudden loadings of thousands of pounds, stride after stride - these must cause at least some damage in the toughest of tendons. Normally, organic structural materials like bones and tendons repair themselves, and given time, come back stronger than they were originally. But if you fail to notice structural fatigue as it's coming on, or you cover it up, and if you continue on with the exercise that's causing it, then failure is preordained.

Mechanical fatigue occurs more gradually in the tendon, with far less chemical fatigue involved. You work a horse hard today, a few fibers give up the ghost and the repair process begins. In a few days you have a little heat and filling. You cover up that repair process with a leg bandage, keeping the leg "tight." The regular hard workouts continue, causing more damage. You add icing to your daily therapy and the leg looks tight as a drum. More work, more damage. Then, the final big workout or competition and the remaining viable fibers in a few bundles taking the most abuse give way - you've build yourself a nice, juicy bow. You have a hole in the tendon that an ultrasound sector scanner has no trouble finding no matter how much wrapping, firing, blistering, cortisone injecting and Bute feeding you can marshall. If you've injected cortisone before the full bow, then you can thank yourself for hastening the disaster along.

2. Shoeing

Somewhere along the line, we came to the conclusion, or should I say delusion, that we could shoe a horse to deliver whatever style of gait we preferred. We decided that we could enhance performance through certain kinds of shoeing. We decided that we could correct conformational defects through shoeing. And we decided that we could make whatever radical changes we wanted to, overnight. And the horse would love it. Mother Nature would love it. Do you know who really appreciates this particular conceit of ours? The drug companies. The vets wielding firing irons and needles. The medicine men. And, of course, the replacement shoer, who can rail for hours about the horrific job the last shoer did on your horse.

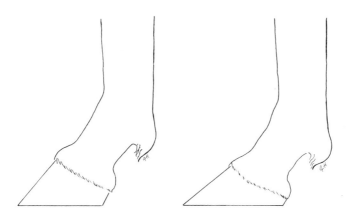

Here you have a normal toe on the left and a long toe on the right. *(Illustration by Judy Hanson)*

As far as the flexor tendons are concerned, the problem is Clown Shoes - long toes, low, underslung heels and, in many racehorses, toe grabs. It is routine to clip the heels and elongate the toes of racehorses because someone erroneously concluded, probably back in the 16th century, that this shoeing configuration provided for a longer stride. If you want to see an instant double bow, take a horse with 52 degree hoof angles in front, lower them to 48s, and slap on a pair of shoes with toe grabs - then roll out a nice hard workout. If you've been very careful with your Thoroughbred or Quarter Horse, bringing it along slowly at the farm with long gallops and keeping reasonably short toes and decent angles, then you'll get a nasty surprise within weeks of sending the horse to the racetrack. I've seen toe angles all the way down to 44 degrees on the racetrack - and I've seen hundreds of bows that could be directly attributed to this kind of shoeing.

But show shoeing can be just as bad. Built-up shoes that lift the hooves 4 inches off the ground in order to get that special exaggerated Park look to the stride are nearly as bad - if the horse tries to make speed on those feet, he'll injure himself. If the horse simply works too long at one time and experiences a little fatigue, bows become likely. While breakdowns in the show ring are not nearly as common as those on the racetrack, they do occur and this is one of the key reasons.

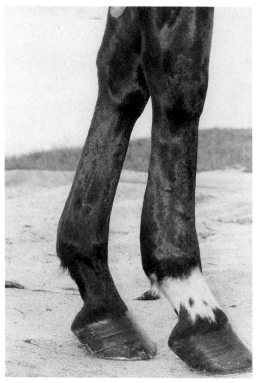

This bowed horse's toes are too long and his heels are slightly underslung - at least he has heels!
(Photo by Suzie Oldham)

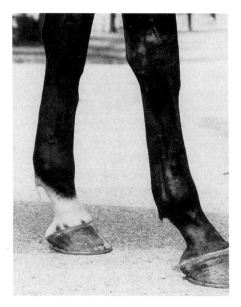

An example of low, underslung heels and low hoof angles. In this case, the farrier has begun attempts at correction by extending the shoes slightly beyond the heel and slightly wide at the heel.
(Photo by Suzie Oldham)

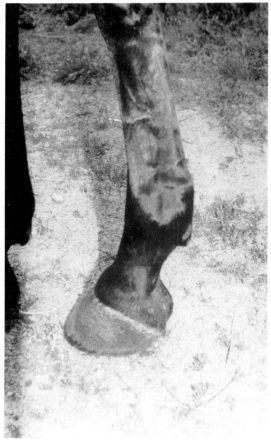

A reasonably good trimming job. Notice how the hoof supports the pastern angle which, in turn, supports the column of bones above. Compare this foot with the "clown shoes" worn by most racehorses.

(Photo by Judy Hanson)

Here are some basic shoeing parameters you should keep in mind. Hoof angles should measure somewhere in the neighborhood of 53 degrees in front and 54 degrees behind. A medium-sized (15 - 15 1/2 hands) horse is probably going to be most comfortable with a toe no longer than 3 1/2 inches, measured from the hairline to the tip of the toe. Some big horses (over 16 hands) will have feet big enough for 4 inch toes. Save the 5 inch toes for elephants. Meanwhile, the heel should drop to the ground at a sharper (steeper) angle than the toe. A hoof with a 53 degree toe angle will probably do well with a 60 degree heel angle.

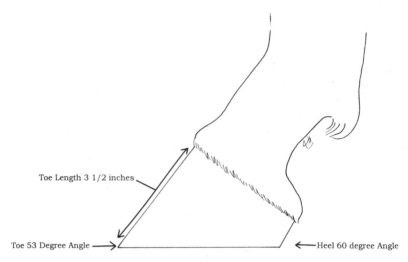

Toe Length 3 1/2 inches

Toe 53 Degree Angle ———→

←——Heel 60 degree Angle

The properly trimmed hoof, with a 53 degree hoof angle and proportionate heel. *(Illustration by Judy Hanson)*

Another trick of the shoeing trade that is a problem for most breeds is "horseing the shoe." The farrier puts on a shoe that is too small, then shaves down the excess hoof wall to make a very pretty fit. Over time, the foot loses its mass and can't take the pounding of regular work. Quarter cracks and contracted heels are two likely results. In fact, because the shoer invariably curls the ends of the shoes under the heels in his desire to be "neat," underslung contracted heels are the common deadly (as far as the tendons are concerned) result.

As horsemen we need to be far more aware of the anatomy of the horse, of his biomechanics, of his body chemistry at rest and during high intensity exercise. We have to know about the forces impacting his body and ensure that he is fully capable of handling them. Big, stupid mistakes are not what kills horses. It's the lack of attention to detail, to the little things, that eventually leads us to catastrophic injury.

For example, one filly I trained had an old check ligament injury that would flare up occasionally. When it did, we had to back off and give it time to pull itself together. After a few instances of this annoying problem, we discovered that when her toes grew out more than 1/8th of an inch, the check flared up. If we shod her every three weeks, before that extra growth occurred, we eliminated the problem. Even after we knew we had the solution, there were times when one thing or another caused us to miss this important shoeing date, and the check came back to haunt us every time.

Another case. A very nice filly was training well in Kentucky but showing occasional tendinitis. The trainer there, who I respected as a knowledgeable, careful horseman, sent her to us in California with very definite shoeing parameters and a warning about her tendinitis. We continued with her training for several months, keeping her feet trimmed as per instructions, and never saw the first sign of tendon problems. Then we sent her to the racetrack (Bay Meadows) for a few workouts just prior to her debut as a racehorse. She worked out once and came back to us with a double bow - the farrier decided her feet didn't look right on the morning of the first workout and, despite our explicit and detailed instructions, shod her to his liking. Just a couple of degrees lower hoof angles. At the time, it was illegal in California to give these guys their just rewards, so I've had to settle for annoying them in print whenever possible. Of course, few of them read - it's frustrating.

3. Unnatural Demands

For some reason, the natural capabilities of the horse and the beauty exhibited in the normal flowing motion of the natural gaits of our horses are not enough for us. Our own private Death Wishes seem to force us to pass on the risks to our horses. Hunting, jumping and eventing contests often seem designed to injure all but the superior athletes - or the luckiest. We trot horses at speeds that most can't gallop. We race horses over surfaces that motocrossers would avoid. We wring the last ounce of effort from our animals in almost every sport we've designed for them.

Insurance rates for jockeys are higher than for skyscraper iron workers, and for good reason. But far more horses die on our racetracks than do jockeys. And while some sportsmen and women die in rodeos, horse shows and 3-day events, far more horses bite the dust training for and competing in these contests. The only real justice levied against us is that we pay dearly for the privilege of killing and crippling expensive animals.

Tendons were designed by nature to take a lot of abuse for a long time - in the same way that the suspension system of a Cadillac is meant to absorb punishment. But we ask the horse to do what nature never intended, what the horse would never do on his own. How many times do you think you could drop a Cadillac from 10 to 12 feet off the ground before something gave in the suspension? How far can you drive a Cadillac through a dry rocky river bed at 1/3 maximum speed? How fast and how far can you take a Cadillac on square wheels? How far can you drive a Cadillac in first gear with the pedal to the floor before it blows up? You see, we don't do things like that to our Cadillacs or our Silverado Duallys. But we do them to our stupidly obedient horses. And we call it Pleasure, Pride of Ownership, Sport.

While it is true that living things can be hardened, through conditioning, to withstand a lot of the punishment we ask them to absorb, very few horsemen bother to bring an animal to the level of fitness where some of these tasks can be survived over the long term. Instead, we run our horses into the ground and go back and buy more.

Later, we're going to look at the ways conditioning can prevent bows, but for now, let's consider ways to avoid the unnatural circumstances that will bring our animal to its knees. For example, if you enter an event, ship in, and find that the course is too dangerous - the jumps too high, the running surface too hard, the obstacles too tough - why not consider sitting this one out? If you enter a horse in a race, then the weather gets so bad that the track is plain slop or hard as cement, why not just scratch and come back another day? Just because 100 or more fools are going to go out and cripple their horses doesn't mean you have to. If they all decided to drive their Silverados into the brick wall at the entrance to the facility, would you feel compelled to do so too?

Not only do we ask the horse to perform unnaturally, but we then "doctor" him up when parts of his body start to complain. Pain is a natural result of injury and it's there for a reason. It's Nature's way of getting the horse to take it easy while the healing process is at work. If we cover it up with pain killers and corticosteroid injections, or leg wraps and ice, and then go on with training, competition or racing, we're begging for disaster. In racing, we can see the stark evidence of that kind of disaster quite regularly on national television.

Now, some people condemn racing as cruel and dangerous. But racing isn't inherently destructive - it depends on how it's practiced. The top trainers don't hurt their racehorses at all. Perhaps the best example is Dr. Len Thomas of Alberta, Canada. Len trains and races Standardbreds and recently retired several at their oldest legal racing age, 14, all sound and ready to race tomorrow, all with more than 400 starts on their charts. All winners. All smiling.

Charlie Whittingham is another example of a trainer who takes his time with young horses, uses no toe grabs, and uses female riders (who don't try to outwrestle their mounts). He's known for long-lasting, sound horses.

Charlie's philosophy differs from most Thoroughbred trainers in that most of the rest train for early speed. So 25-month-old Thoroughbreds are asked to go as fast as they can for five furlongs long before cartilage, tendons, and ligaments have strengthened enough to stand the forces they'll encounter. Those of you training other performance horses will be astonished to know that Thoroughbreds typically get five minutes of ontrack exercise a day. Many Thoroughbred trainers don't believe a horse can safely gallop more than 2 miles in a day. Weird, eh?

But then, you guys and gals jump horses over 5 1/2 foot jumps, down into quagmires, bang them into wooden poles and 50 gallon drums, hook them to carts and chariots, and take them on the occasional 50 or 100 mile jaunt. Horses don't do those kinds of things on purpose in the wild. These are unnatural activities for the horse, and our primary job is to prepare them properly before we ask for a competitive performance.

4. Sudden Stress

As I'll detail later, tendons respond to stress by becoming stronger, as long as that stress is brought on gradually. And most of us with any horsesense whatsoever understand this principle. We take our time, watch our horses carefully, and bring on the workload gradually - sometimes too gradually. By that, I mean we sometimes tend to go too slowly in the beginning and then suddenly figure out that we're 30 days away from competition and then get ourselves into a rush catching up to our horse's date with destiny. But, for the most part, we're careful.

Sometimes, what seems natural and logical isn't. I had a nice trotter in training named Clyde Bloom. He could lay down seven straight miles at a 2:30 rate and not blow out a candle afterward. The Ohio State track coach and I were experimenting with interval training and we were building this animal for tough workouts to follow with these semi-hard Long Slow Distance workouts. All the trainers at the Delaware, Ohio racetrack kept asking us when we were going to turn the horse the right way of the track and "train" him. Everything we'd done thus far was in the opposite direction from the racing direction - that's the tradition in Standardbred training, do your slow work the "wrong way" and work fast the "right way."

One day the coach and I concluded that what the other trainers were asking us to do was logical. After all, human athletes often had time trials, where they ran fast at racing distance and the coaches could see how far along they were. So, we turned Clyde Bloom the right way and let him roll. It was a very nice mile, down around 2:00, and he wasn't tired at the end. But in the process he tore apart his left hind medial suspensory ligament and was instantly retired. With all those miles the wrong way, this suspensory branch was not ready for a whole new set of mechanics going fast the right way of the track. We understood the logic of the problem about thirty seconds too late.

At one time, we had a group of 20 Thoroughbreds in training down in Greenwood, Delaware on a farm track. We were doing some aggressive workouts in our first interval training experience with runners. Every four days we'd be shooting 6 X 3/8ths miles with short rest periods between each heat. We were checking heartrate recoveries and had laid down more than 600 miles of progressively loaded exercise on each horse before moving into these workouts. We kept track of everything. Fifteen of the horses made it through fine. Five came up with injuries - knee chips, ankle chips and bows.

Later, we went over our workouts and heartrate recoveries, toe lengths, hoof angles, shoe types - everything. We ran linear regressions on the factors we could put numbers to. We got one strong correlation: the horses that were injured were increasing their speeds each workout .3 seconds faster than those which stayed sound. All eventually were asked for the same speeds, but these five had delivered just a little bit sooner than the rest. From that experience, we learned to hold the horses back from rapid increases in speed. These days, we don't get that kind of injury - unless, for some reason, the horse gets away and goes too fast, too soon. Then, we sit with our fingers crossed for three or four days, waiting for that tendon or knee to say hello.

People think it's uncanny that they can be telling me on the phone all about a horse I've never seen, workouts, toe lengths, angles, heartrate recoveries, and in the middle of the conversation I'll say, "Whoops, you bowed her right there, didn't you?" They'll say, no, it happened a couple days later, when she was doing absolutely nothing, she must have done it in the stall, and I'll say, "Nope, you bowed her right there and it showed up a couple of days later." Sometimes they're insulted and sometimes they think I'm some kind of genius. Far from it. I've done the same stupid thing enough times to know better. That's all. It's the little stupid things that kill you. Stuff you don't even notice while you're doing it. Stuff that everybody else does routinely. Stuff that cripples their horses, too.

But there are other ways to bring on sudden increases in stress without simply going too fast, too soon. For example, let's say we're in the middle of background mileage with a horse - we've built him up to 4 continuous miles at a 3:00 per mile rate and he's perfectly happy to deliver that kind of work. In fact, we're thinking of bumping him another half mile tomorrow. But tonight it rains cats and dogs. Tomorrow, instead of cutting into the galloping surface an inch or two, this horse is going to dig down four to five inches with every step - real soggy. We decide not to add the extra half. We give him his usual four, he struggles, goes slower, and comes off the work surface blowing - not staggering or shaking, just blowing. He worked hard, but he's not really fatigued.

Have we hurt him? Probably. Three days later we'll likely see some filling and detect some heat in the ankles or up into the tendon. Tendinitis. Why? Because the stresses that the tendons are encountering with this deep going are a "surprise." The animal's physical capacity to handle the work without fatiguing does not reflect tendon structural strength. The tendons aren't muscles; they're not building up chemical fatigue. But they are experiencing a lot of extra stretching forces. Even though we let the horse go slower, avoiding chemical fatigue, we're introducing enough structural stress that it's probably not a good idea to take the horse for the full mileage over the soggy surface. Best policy is to cut the mileage in half until the weather permits easier going. Of course, if there's going to be slipping and sliding, stay off the surface entirely.

The same factors are at play when you move a horse from a firm turf surface to a deep sand or dirt surface - as from the farm to a racetrack. Soft surfaces will abuse soft tissues like tendons, ligaments and muscles. Remember, hard surfaces, if they're going to produce injury, do so in the feet, the bones and cartilage of the ankles, knees and hocks or in the cannon bones. Making speed over uneven surfaces puts all parts at risk.

Sudden stress is not limited to track surfaces. Let's say we've discovered that our last trainer had the angles of our horse down around 48 degrees with long toes. We corrected that in a hurry, snipping off lots of toe and raising the angles to 52 degrees in front. Can we now go out and safely lay down a nice long gallop at good speed?

Nope. Under normal circumstances, raising the angle takes some stress off the superficial flexor tendon, but adds stress to the deep flexor. With those 48s, it is likely that the animal's gait was severely compromised and that both the deep and superficial were taking punishment due to delayed breakover. You'd do well not to make such gigantic changes, and certainly not to believe you can go out and really drill the horse having "solved" his shoeing problem. Your deep flexor is liable to start complaining. Instead, change the feet only a couple of degrees at a time, no matter how far off they are. And sneak back into the workload gradually, keeping your eye on the tendons. Every three or four weeks, you can attack the angle problem again.

5. Concussion

As far as the tendons are concerned, rapid increases in concussion can affect both the superficial and the deep flexor tendons, not so much by stretching them as by whipping them in the same way as you can snake a rope along the ground with flips of your wrist. If you're lucky, you'll see the results of this whipping back and forth up where the check ligament connects with the deep digital flexor, a couple of inches under the knee. There will be a thickening, sometimes quite hard, in the channel between the superficial digital flexor tendon and the cannon bone. Here's what's going wrong:

Hold your first and second fingers out in front of you and spread them apart. See that webbing of skin at the base of them? That's what the check ligament looks like as it wraps around the deep digital flexor tendon. I don't know if you've ever cut yourself in the webbing between your fingers or between your toes, but the cut takes forever to heal. That's the way it is with checks. They get better, they get worse, they get better and they get worse. Generally, they don't make the horse lame by themselves, but if the swelling gets bad, the horse will feel them. Eventually, a lump of scar tissue will form at the intersection of the check and the deep digital flexor tendon, and that's about as good as things are going to get.

A check ligament problem tells you that the tendons are snapping, whipping or oscillating - whatever you want to call it - and that damage to the superficial and deep digital flexor tendons is likely if you don't change what you're doing. The concussion that is causing the trouble can come from hard surfaces, but also from feet that are too small or hoof angles that are too high. If you can discover the cause, correct it, but don't go crazy. Drop the angles too far, or drop into real deep going, and you're back to the over-stretching problem.

Toe grabs also increase the rate that force is applied to the leg when the foot hits the ground - that is, concussion. Ideally, the hoof is supposed to be moving rearward in relation to the rest of the body when it hits the ground. The hoof is also supposed to slide forward for a couple of microseconds when it touches down. This lessens concussion. Fatigue shortens the stride and tends to catch the foot early with touchdown, before it begins its rearward swing. Add to that unfortunate circumstance the stopping power of the toe grab and you have a wonderful opportunity for one structure or another to fail because of a concussive overload. You could take a sledgehammer to the bottom of the hoof and not deliver as much concussive force.

Or, we've just gone to a seminar where a highly qualified veterinary researcher tells us the following: Bones get stronger with high levels of concussion. Therefore, if you want strong cannon bones in your horses, all babies should begin training with little short bursts of speed scattered about each day's workout. Not many, just a couple, not long, just a hundred yards or so. Can we safely take his advice? In a word, no.

If you start showing the baby short little sprints, you may get some grand bone development, but it will be at the expense of at least two other systems. While it is true that bone remodels itself with stress, i.e. concussion, you cannot remodel the bones of a young horse without putting other structures at risk. Tendons and ligaments strengthen with repeated flexions, not sudden concussions. And the mind of the baby is volatile, to say the least. Babies love speed. Give them a little, they want more. Start sticking these little bursts of speed into a baby every day and pretty soon you have a Mutant Ninja on your hands, with a mouth getting sore, an attitude going south, and tendons starting to cry out for a more intelligent approach.

If you want concussion, try pavement. In England and Australia, horses often walk and trot out to the gallops over paved roads, a mile or so each way. Their trainers believe that their bones benefit from the shock, and that may be so. At least speed isn't being introduced early and adding a whole bunch of mechanical variables to the equation. Besides, I don't think bone and cartilage react the same way to sudden concussions. And, aside from bucked shins, your biggest concern with bones in the young horse is abnormal cartilage wear. That's where "knees" and "ankles" and "hocks" originate, as the immature cartilage in this joints is squashed, rubbed away and torn before it has a chance to thicken and harden.

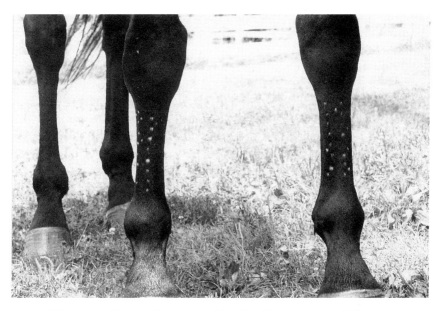

What are "knees" and "ankles"? Here - one of the walking wounded, with four flat tires, pin fired in a vain demonstration that "someone cares." Someone should have cared a few months earlier.

(Photo by Suzie Oldham)

47

If you want to avoid bucked shins entirely, save the massive changes in bone for later, after you've got a few hundred miles of Long Slow Distance into those tendons and ligaments. The bone will be happy to oblige, whenever you introduce higher concussive stresses. Even then, start long and slow and introduce shorter and faster works over time. When playing God, exercise restraint.

6. Accidents

How 'bout them hotwalkin' machines? Save a lot of labor don't they? Save a lot of money for the trainer, too. Why, you can't imagine how much exercise you can get into a horse on a hot walker. Just as long as you keep the BB gun handy.

The hotwalking machine is a disaster waiting to happen. Sure, you can hotwalk a hundred horses before one acts up or gets loose, or two get into a fight, spinning around, trying to kick each other. But it will happen. Then somebody has to pay the vet bill and take the loss in horseflesh.

Actually, there is no exercise reason for hotwalking machines. No horse, properly warmed down after exercise, needs to be walked at all upon returning to the barn. Horses are hung on these devices so that the groom can clean the stall. That's the sole justification for them. Substituting hotwalking for exercise, especially on days after a hard workout or competition, is absolutely the wrong thing to do. Unless you're a gyp trainer, or an owner willing to pay only gyp training fees. In such cases, both parties are getting their just rewards.

Stall webbings are dangerous devices. If you want your horse to get a nice top-to-bottom breeze in the hot weather, then buy metal mesh stall doors that go top to bottom. Otherwise, that nice, smart but curious animal you've invested your dreams in is someday going to get tangled up in the web and he'll bow a tendon, or worse.

Standing bandages are another risky habit. Big, fluffy white bandages protecting the legs - that's what it looks like. Sure looks like somebody is really taking care of the horse. But, to the horse, bandages are sometimes a toy, sometimes an irritant, and always a threat to the tendons. They call it "cording", but it's really just a bowed tendon caused by part of the bandage getting too tight, shutting off the circulation, and causing the death of adjacent tendon tissue. Necrosis. And standing bandages can be dangerous even if the horse never bothers them - with bandages and poultices keeping the legs "tight", you can't see oncoming tendon problems until they're severe. Standing bandages do nothing to prevent bowed tendons. They only mask conditions that should not be masked.

Leaving the horse in his stall so he can't hurt himself is another accident waiting to happen. Inconsistent day-to-day exercise is not only the most common cause of tying up, but also leads to misbehavior in a reasonably fit horse. Contrary to popular belief, horses prefer exercise to stall time. With no regular exercise, the horse's concept of the stall as "home" changes to one of the stall as "jail." When they get out of jail, they want to dance, and prance, and raise all sorts of hell. This is when you get a "rap" - another form of bowed tendon. In this case, the misbehaving horse clips himself in the tendon, causing traumatic tearing of the tissues that has exactly the same result as if the tendon were injured through fatigue or a misstep. And sometimes the horse doesn't even need freedom to raise hell - all he has to do is step into his water bucket in order to attract your undivided attention.

And then there are all the structures we have around, cluttering up the horse's environment. A lot of horses injure their tendons going in and out of swimming pools (or trying to climb out the side). They get hurt going on and off treadmills and aquatic treadmills. Even a loading ramp is a dangerous apparatus with a fractious horse. Concrete or wooden steps going in and out of stalls. Slippery surfaces in or near wash stalls. Slippery surfaces where a galloping horse might encounter them.

If you really want to see a sore tendon, try the loose shoes trick. Don't check the feet every day - just wait until a problem comes up before you bother. What you're liable to get is a shoe that comes half off, either slipping under the coffin bone to snap it or hanging out to one side to slice through the contralateral tendon. Delightful.

Are you beginning to see the importance of details? Too often we get into a routine with our horses that doesn't recognize their individual differences, that doesn't notice their individual aches and pains. Good horsemanship comes from having lived with horses long enough to notice all the little signs, all the little details, that lesser beings simply take for granted. When you become a horseman, you can be very proud of the accomplishment. Most who call themselves horsemen are not. And these are the ones who make the same blunders time after time. You and I can't afford these kinds of mistakes. Once is enough. Learn from mine and you can avoid a whole lot of sorrow and expense.

7. Conformation

This is the least of your worries, but it's an excuse I've heard quite often - the horse was destined to bow because of conformation or inbred structural traits. Bowed tendons are man-made, for the most part.

Still, there are plenty of vets and trainers around who will be glad to say that your horse was predisposed to bow because of one or another conformational defects. Usually, it's long, sloping pasterns that come in for criticism. At present, there isn't enough research to support or deny this contention, but if your horse has long sloping pasterns, it's all the more reason to avoid all the other causes outlined in this section.

8. Trainer Failure to Heed Early Warnings

Many bows occur long after the trainer has had ample warning that doom is impending. My experience with racehorse trainers is that they want to keep going with a horse, hiding its problems from the owner, from the horse, from the vet, and, eventually, from themselves. They act pained and put out when the horse finally develops a full-blown bow, and they'll try to tell the owner that they "seen it coming."

While greed plays some part in these bows, with the trainer trying to extract all the "day money" he can, most of the problem is plain stupidity. These guys don't know why the bows are happening, they don't keep track of anything they do with exercise and shoeing, they don't do enough of the right kinds of exercise, and they have trouble remembering where they live. Their whole job, it seems to them, is to cover up everything they're doing wrong, while waiting for that miracle horse, the one that runs like the wind and that you can't hurt with a .44 magnum. And when the inevitable happens, they expect the vet to rush in and bail them out with some quick cure. Never happens.

9. Indifference: Owners, Trainers and the Industry in General

It is the horse owner's responsibility to see that his animals are cared for and trained by competent handlers. The owner should visit the training facility frequently, during working hours and after hours. He should walk in unannounced, and any trainer who doesn't like that approach should be dismissed. The owner must see the real thing, the actual working environment and work processes his animal goes through every day. No staged "owner shows."

If the owner fails to stay close to his animals, then he deserves the consequences. If the owner fails to take action when he sees carelessness or overly aggressive behavior in the handling of his animals, then he must reap the whirlwind of his own indifference. If the owner doesn't know enough about horses to pass judgment on a trainer, then he should learn or stick to dude ranches for his equine pleasure.

Wouldn't you expect the veterinary profession to adopt preventive measures to insure the safety of horse and rider in all competitive events - rather than simply trying to put Humpty Dumpty back together again after the fact, or covering up injuries that will automatically result in catastrophes later on? As you can see, all of the genuine causes of bowed tendons are avoidable, depending on how smart and how careful we are with our animals. When I say "we," I mean we, because I've caused my share of bows, too. That's what experience is: mistakes. They say you have to make about 3,000 of them before you're any good at your profession. And maybe that's why some professionals call their job a "practice." And why malpractice insurance premiums are so high.

Isn't it reasonable to assume that the trainer's job includes preparing the animal to the extent that he can compete safely, without fear of cataclysmic injury to horse or rider? If injuries like bowed tendons are preventable, then why don't the owners of these animals sue their trainers when $10,000 to $10 million investments turn to dust in an instant? Well, they'd have to prove negligence. And to do that, they'd have to show that the trainer didn't follow recognized, industry-standard procedures in training the animal. There's the rub: industry standards are what cripples almost every equine athlete. Too often, when a trainer tells me he has 20 years of experience handling horses, I'm led to conclude that he has one year of experience and 19 years of repeating that initial experience. One hundred and fifty mistakes, repeated for twenty years, is not 3,000 mistakes; it's still the same 150. We do the same damned stupid thing, over and over again, and we get the same damned injuries, over and over again.

We're all very lucky that horses can't sue.

If horse owners simply refuse to compete under unsafe circumstances, race unsound horses or condone abusive practices, then the trainers, vets and organizers of these events will slowly get the message. Very slowly, because some trainers don't give a damn if they cripple your horses, and all these people have pressures from the other side to either put on a show or get shoved down the list for special favors from the powers that be. Horse owners must speak up, preferably with their checkbooks.

Now, don't take this as a blanket condemnation all of officials, vets, trainers and shoers. I know there are a legion of each category who put the horses first and know what they're doing. The problem is that the bad apples give their colleagues a bad name.

The whole idea of making mistakes is to learn from

them - you start out with big, dumb blunders and, over time, you refine your approach, the mistakes get smaller and less damaging. The first step in avoiding injury is discovering why the injury occurs. The goal in training performance horses should be to avoid all injuries entirely. Easier said than done. But possible.

---

1. Dr. Ian Silver, Dr. Peter Rossdale, et al, *A clinical and experimental study of tendon injury, healing and treatment in the horse*, University of Bristol, supplement to The Equine Veterinary Journal (July, 1983).

Chapter 6: The Signs of Impending Disaster

The unfortunate aspect of superficial digital flexor tendon tears is that they are extremely subtle when they begin to occur, and then come on all of a sudden when a large number of fibers suddenly give way during a hard workout. I've seen horses walking, trotting and galloping on full-blown bows with no signs of lameness. Before you've actually got a bow, you'll seldom get a warning of one coming on by the gait of the horse.

A bow most often seems like a sudden happening, unless you're paying strict attention to the legs of your animal every day. The very first sign of an oncoming bow is going to be that the tendon just doesn't look as perfectly straight as it did yesterday. No real thickening, no swelling - it's just not quite as straight.

Three days later, there may be some heat and a little side-to-side sponginess at a point where a tiny bump may become barely noticeable, usually midway down the tendon. That's a bow. It's very localized at the onset, and if you catch it then, it will stay localized and heal more quickly - healing time is directly related by the extend of the damage incurred. Minor injuries require about three days to really make themselves evident. A bump that appears two or three days after a hard piece of work is still a "bow", but healing is likely to be quicker (six months as opposed to more than a year) than a major tear. If you perform a hard workout and you've got an easily seen bump by the time you get back to the barn, you've got big trouble. Once you have a couple inches of hot, swollen, protruding tendon, you're in for it.

Deep flexor problems tend to be low, and no real bump can be seen while the horse is standing - just thickness above the fetlock. But if you lift the leg and flex it, you can feel the superficial and the deep tendons, and a torn deep flexor will have a knot on it much like the bump on a bowed superficial flexor. Suspensory problems will generally exist even lower, down where the suspensory attaches to the wrap-around annular ligament. Suspensory injuries are likely to look like a "flat tire," and are usually one-sided, with a fatness on the inside or on the outside of the ankle. With a severe deep flexor injury, the bulge is behind, can be seen from both sides, and begins just above the sesamoids. Unfortunately, the beginnings of deep flexor trouble at the fetlock level are difficult to catch - that annular ligament does a good job of keeping preliminary deep flexor problems out of sight and out of mind.

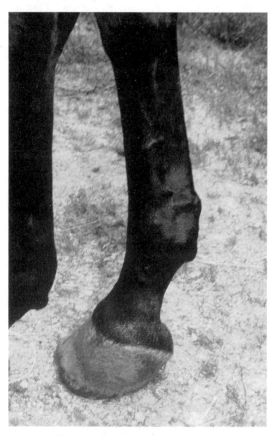

This low bow may not involve the superficial digital flexor tendon. This kind of swelling could indicate deep flexor, annular ligament or sesamoid injury. Without an ultrasound scan, it is impossible to know which structures are injured and how badly.

(Photo by Judy Hanson)

Still, any time you see the beginnings of a rounding of the ankle, especially one ankle and not the other, the deep flexor must be considered a suspect. Not a likely suspect, but a suspect nonetheless. Remember, a torn tendon often begins as minor damage that will heal quickly. If you don't heed the early warning signs, though, you'll get a big tear that will take more than a year to heal. When the ankles start to get fat, back off and wait for them to return to normal. If they do, you go back to work, and the ankles start looking at you again, call in a vet with an ultrasound sector scanner and get an accurate diagnosis.

Unfortunately, an oncoming lesion on the deep digital flexor tendon causes even less apparent lameness than does an oncoming bow. And I've seen horses that still walked, trotted, cantered and played as if nothing were wrong at all.

There's another telling sign that your horse is putting the stretch on his tendons. He'll dig a hole and then stand on the side of it, so that his toes are lower than his heels - resting his tendons. You're right on the ragged edge of disaster at that point. Eliminate the cause (generally long toes and low heels), give him a little time to recover (a couple of easy weeks) and then go back to work.

Every trainer worth his or her salt, palpates the tendons of his horses every morning before the horses go out to work. Sometimes it's a cursory exam, running the thumb and forefinger down the outside of the tendons, exerting some pressure, looking for bumps, irregularities, or heat and swelling. Any kind of thickening or heat is cause to pick up the hoof and palpate more aggressively, pinching the tendons, both superficial and deep, all along their length, looking for a reaction from the horse

So, every morning, you should run your fingers over the tendons of your horse, first, flat down the back of the tendons and then pinching the tendon between your thumb and forefinger and sliding your fingers down the sides of the tendon. Then, use your thumb and forefinger to slide back down the area between the superficial flexor and the cannon bone - thickness here indicates either suspensory or deep flexor problems. Even if there is no reaction, it's best to ease off the workload until all the signs disappear. Then come back slowly and cautiously. Yes, it's tedious, and you miss races or competitions, but you're saving yourself a lot of trouble.

In general, heat that keeps coming on is trouble, while heat that comes and goes is normal wear and tear, stress and recovery. But if you can feel heat with your bare hand, pay close attention to the area and back off the work at least until the heat is completely gone. Because I've dealt with valuable racehorses, I've had owners who've purchased infrared thermography heat detectors for me to use with their animals. The machine is called a Hughes Probeye (available now as the FLIR Systems TVS 3000). The Probeye has become a crutch for me because I can see all sorts of oncoming problems, including potential bows, two weeks to a month before they get ugly. The human hand can feel a temperature change of about 5 degrees centigrade, while the Hughes Probeye can "see" heat patterns in 0.5 degree increments.

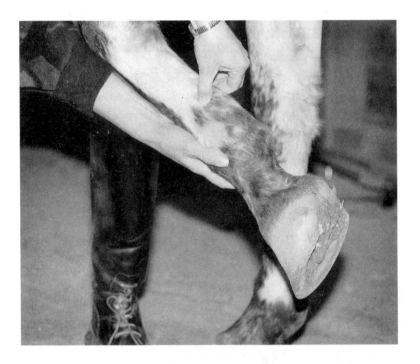

Palpating the superficial and deep flexor tendons, feeling for a bump while watching the horse for pain reaction. (*Photo by Judy Hanson*)

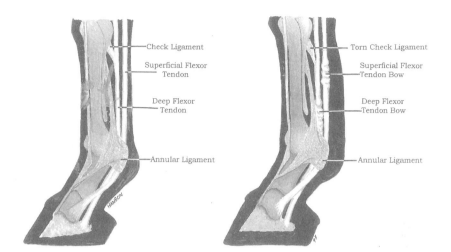

Check Ligament

Superficial Flexor Tendon

Deep Flexor Tendon

Annular Ligament

Torn Check Ligament

Superficial Flexor Tendon Bow

Deep Flexor Tendon Bow

Annular Ligament

The foreleg on the left shows the tendons and ligaments you are palpating. On the right, the artist's rendering of damage to the superficial and the deep digital flexor tendon, and to the check ligament.

(Illustration by Judy Hanson)

The warmest part of the lower leg is normally the coronary band at the hairline of the hoof. The rest of the leg, up to the knee, is several degrees cooler. Between the cannon bone and the tendons is a thin area where blood vessels are active and near the skin surface. This channel will be warmer than the surrounding tissues, but still cooler than the coronary band.

Let's say that the temperature of the coronary band is 30 degrees C. The ankle area is going to be about 26 degrees C, and the circulatory channel between the cannon bone and the tendons might be 28 degrees. If you have a tendon injury, the affected area of the tendon is going to display a temperature approaching that of the coronary band on the same leg. In fact, there will be a "thermal bump" right at the point of the tear in a superficial flexor tendon. On either side of this bump, the tendon temperature will be a degree or two cooler.

With a thermal video system like the Probeye, the

circulatory channel will appear to bulge out where the tendon is injured, or the entire tendon will be warmer than the circulatory channel, with a hot "bump" on the tendon at the site of the tear.

Deep flexor tendon injuries are more difficult to locate because they tend to be low, down where the tendons and the suspensory and annular ligaments all gather together. Check ligament injuries can be confused with heat put out by a splint, because the check lies high and closer to the cannon bone than the flexor tendons. Here, though, there is usually a localized swelling or thickness that is easily palpated.

This early warning system pays for itself in about six months in a small racing stable. I haven't bowed a horse in years - knock on wood - even though I'm always running into preliminary signs of oncoming trouble. It's always give and take, give and take

Every little indication is not something to go running to the vet about. There are hand held infrared thermometers available for under $1,000 and, if you get one of these, I can sell you a video tape of normal and abnormal heat patterns in horses with oncoming or existing problems. You can bring on exercise until the leg parts start to become warm, then back off until the heat disappears.

But when you get persistent heat, or heat and swelling, or a bump on a tendon, or any kind of mushiness around the tendon, it's time to call in the vet for a complete diagnosis, including ultrasound sector scanning. A hundred dollars spent here can save you thousands of dollars in lost time and ruined animals.

At this point, you should have a pretty good feel for the physiology (what happens) and etiology (cause) of bowed tendons. In the following chapters, we're going to take a look at healing and rehabilitating the bowed horse. I'm afraid you're going to find it bad news for the most part, but at least you'll fully understand the task before you, should you be forced to deal with the injury.

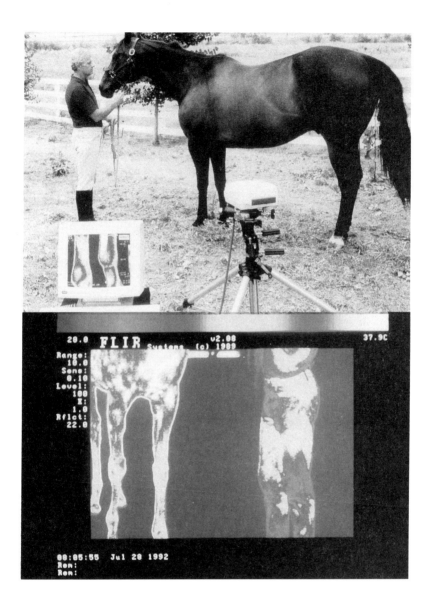

The FLIR TVS 3000 System. Other manufacturers produce similar devices. All these video-based systems sell for more than $20,000 new.

(Photograph courtesy of FLIR Systems, Inc.)

Chapter 7: Treatment and Rehabilitation - The Big Picture

Let's take a look at the most extreme case of tendon healing. For a minute, imagine that something has sliced your horse's tendon in two, halfway down the cannon bone. If you suture the two ends back together, eventually some kind of healing will take place. There will probably be a lot of scar tissue formed, the wound will ooze plasma and dead cells for a while, the whole area will blow up and be hot and painful for a long long time, but, eventually, the severed tendon will grow back together. But it will probably be weak in that area, because scar tissue is weaker and less flexible than tendon tissue. And there will be adhesions, perhaps permanent, between the tendon and its sheath - further limiting the function of the tendon.

Now, a bowed tendon is precisely the same problem, but confined to smaller groups of severed fibers deep within the tendon. The fibers have pulled completely apart, and, instead of the blue sky between them that you get when you sever the whole tendon, you have pockets of blood and dead tissue between the broken ends of the fibers. But the fibers are cut, and they must grow back together again, properly, before the tendon is brand new. Luckily, not all the circulation has been disrupted around them, as is the case in a complete severing of the tendon. And there are nearby fibers that are still holding, if only tenuously.

These still-connected fibers allow the horse to bear some weight on the injured tendon. In time, the good fibers will allow the horse to actually flex the leg and walk - later, trot. With the whole fibers as a guide and the flexions of the leg a stimulus, tendon fibers will eventually regenerate properly, in line with stress, and you'll get a healing that is not mostly scar tissue. It'll take more than a year for this to happen.

The healing of a small scratch or cut on your skin is a minor miracle. A multitude of specialized cells and chemicals cooperate in the sealing off of the damaged area, carting off dead or damaged tissues, fighting off infection, and, finally, reconstructing the original architecture as closely as possible. Depending on the extent of the damage, and how many different layers of skin the wound penetrates, the area may completely regenerate, or you may be left with a scar, an indentation where certain tissues were unable to come back, or limited use of the body part.

The healing of a ruptured tendon is a major miracle when compared to the healing of a superficial cut. This intricate process requires time, along with very carefully considered handling. Tendons are complex organs with several distinct types of tissues involved. Buried within the body, they hold major parts of the body together, and have a limited blood supply. There are no instant solutions or radical interventions that will save the day. Let's take a closer look at the process itself.

When tendon fibers tear, there is internal bleeding. The blood supply for both flexor tendons is provided by blood vessels within the tendons themselves and by blood vessels contained in their sheaths or paratenons. When tendon fibers tear, internal bleeding results and pockets of coagulated blood (hematomas) can form. (It is these pockets, or holes, that the ultrasound sector scanner sees when the vet is diagnosing the extent of the damage to a tendon. In order for the tendon to heal, all the debris, including the coagulated blood, must be removed from the area. For as long as the holes appear in the ultrasound scan, the tendon is far from healed. Once the holes are filled in with collagen fibers, there is still the necessity for those fibers to become mature, tough fibers.) The body's first reaction is to try to immobilize the joint and take pressure off the torn tissues. Heat, swelling, pain - those are the initial weapons nature brings into play. The horse goes lame and stays off the injured leg.

Immediately after the injury to the tendon fibers, damaged tissue dies and the immune system sends white cells and catabolic (protein eating) enzymes to the site to clean up the mess. The body gets rid of the debris that results from injury by sending in clean-up cells to digest it and carry it away. But the clean-up operation, and other reactions to the injury, cause heat, swelling, pain, and further disruption of the tendon fibers. Not only is the body sending rescue units to the area via the bloodstream, but it is also attempting to immobilize the joint and prevent the animal's use of it until the repair process is well underway. But this immune response can do a lot of damage all by itself.

Why does the horse display an "overactive" immune system? Horses in the wild don't know what bed rest is. While horses running free, under no pressure from predators, are very unlikely to bow, there are circumstances under which a tendon can become injured - a fall, a prairie dog hole, a pack of wolves in constant harassment. When such an injury does occur, the wild horse cannot stand still. In fact, an injured horse is the first and primary target of predators in the wild. He'll probably have to run for his life on that bowed tendon. An overactive immune system allows him to do so, to some degree. Swelling and heat immobilize the joints nearby the injury while signaling the horse's mind that something terrible has happened down there and he'd better try running on three legs instead of four for a while. Or avoid running at all when there is no immediate danger. In the confinement of a stall, the horse is protected from predators, but we must protect him from his immune system. At this point, swelling and heat are in the acute phase. Unfortunately, these initial reactions of the immune system do even more damage. The swelling is the most damaging, because it can shut off circulation and cause further necrosis (death) of tendon tissues.

Swelling compromises blood supply and can kill off even more tissues. Although blood is filling the limb, it is not healing the damage. The blood is not circulating; it is pooling and congesting into the swelling you see. Attacking the swelling with cold and with anti-inflammatory drugs may slow healing at first, but will limit the damage done by the horse's overactive immune reaction. Our goal is to limit additional damage and temper the immune reaction. As the initial acute reaction to the injury settles down, repair can begin in earnest.

A soupy pool of necrotic (dead) tissue forms and from it arises the first attempt at repair: granulation tissue.

Granulation tissue is what you see with a wound's initial stage of healing, a proliferation of disorganized tissues we call "proud flesh." Within granulation tissues, cells are being instructed as to how to differentiate and organize to replace injured tissues. In case of the tendon, some will form collagen fibers, others will form blood vessels, and still others will differentiate into contractile, muscle-like cells.

From the granulation tissue, new collagen fibers are formed. These are very thin compared to normal fibers and are made up of immature collagen, Type III (the weakest) predominating. At one month after the injury, most of the necrotic tissue has been removed and has been replaced by this immature connective tissue. New blood vessels have formed to serve the repairing area. Over time, this collagen will gradually thicken and toughen, becoming Type II and finally the original Type I that made up most of the mature tendon before it was injured.

As these fibers become mature, they will develop smaller cross-links between them, knitting them tightly together. This happens with scar tissue collagen, too, but in this case, the mature fibers are woven in a random basket-weave manner which is less able to withstand high locomotive stresses. If scar tissue is allowed to mature and develop cross-links, then it will be very difficult to replace it with normal tendon tissue later on. (See discussion of BAPN in Chapter 11.)

The extent of the tearing of the fibers of the tendon bears directly on how long the tendon is going to take to heal. A latticework of fibers must bridge the gap, allowing for the development of other fibers that are properly aligned. As these fibers are forming and maturing, some light exercise will help to avoid random weaving of fibers. Large areas of damage are not easily bridged. One full year after rupture, a superficial digital flexor tendon will still contain areas of weakness at the site of the original injury. And that means that a once-bowed tendon is likely to bow again, under less stress than when it originally bowed, more than a year after initial injury. This is why bowed horses frequently are not successfully brought back to their original levels of performance.

At three months after injury, the connective tissue matrix is more dense and larger blood vessels are serving the area. It is at this point that the outward appearance of the tendon begins to look "healed". It isn't, though, not by a long shot.

At six months, the scar tissue is becoming more and more like that of normal tendon tissue, the fibers becoming thicker and many maturing into Type I (the strongest) collagen. The larger fibers are more likely to form *intrafibrillar covalent crosslinks*, the same as happens with a good exercise program in normal tendons. Additionally, these fibers are now aligning themselves in line with potential stress loads, and the crimping pattern of the fibers, the zigzag that allows them to stretch, is starting to appear.

At 14 months after injury, the tendon is still not returned to normal, and there is evidence in recent scientific investigations that some of the weaker scar tissue will remain forever. The decision as to when the tendon is as healed as it's ever going to get must be made by the veterinarian and the owner after periodic ultrasound monitoring.

Of course, this healing time span and the degree of recovery depends a great deal on the extent of the original injury - how much cleanup had to be done, how much tissue had to be regenerated, etc. It also depends on how smart or how stupid the external aids to healing, that we humans apply, have been.

Catching a tendon that is sustaining damage early on is the best way to save money and time. If, instead, you cover up an oncoming bow, and keep on doing whatever it is that is causing the tendon to fail, you're begging for big trouble in the very near future. Let's put it this way: you've already got big trouble; you're begging for catastrophe.

Every time you perform strenuous exercise with your horse, some tissue damage occurs, part of it within the tendons. But for as long as the tendon retains its structural integrity, with no bundles of collagen fibers having separated, then it is possible to eliminate the cause and completely repair the damage. You can say the same for muscle soreness as opposed to muscle rupture. Muscle rupture is a very nasty injury, even though muscles are much more likely to heal completely than are tendons. Years after a muscle rupture, there will still be signs of the old injury - usually a dent in the flesh where more scar tissue than muscle tissue is present. And the muscle is subject to reinjury near the inflexible scar tissue - it's worse with a tendon.

Muscle cells are contractile, and "muscle tone" refers to the fact that a well-exercised muscle is always partially contracted when at rest. Thus, when a heavy load is placed upon the muscle, it can, to an extent, be stretched without tearing the muscle fibers. It's one of the benefits of fitness.

Tendon collagen cells are elastic. Within them is a tightly woven zig-zag fibril structure as shown below. With injury and repair, that zig-zag structure is straighter, as in B. Obviously, a fiber in the shape of A has more potential for stretch than does one that is already partially straightened. No matter how mature the eventually "healed" collagen becomes, it will never regain its original stretchability. That's why refitted muscles can withstand more abuse than completely healed tendons.

Prognosis

Guarded. You sell severely bowed horses into careers where they'll never experience the same level of stress that bowed the tendon. Tendons will heal to the point where many activities can be supported, including breeding, pleasure riding, sometimes cross-country and endurance competition. But events involving high speed or jumping big fences are unlikely to leave an old bow in peace.

To be sure, there are some racehorses which have survived bows to go on and race and win. Perhaps these were tendons that had minor injuries in the first place. Quite a few Standardbreds (trotters and pacers), though, have come back from genuine bows. I've seen cases where completely severed tendons healed enough to allow a few Standardbreds to race and win. For the most part, though, a Thoroughbred or Quarter Horse racehorse with a bow is no longer a racehorse, no matter how long you give the horse to recover.

As you'll see in later chapters, we've tried many different healing modes with very little real success - if returning to full racing performance is the measure of success. Even though, after a few months, a bowed tendon may appear to be normal, inside it's made up of immature collagen at the site of the old bow, and, should that collagen eventually mature, it's still going to be less flexible and more easily injured than the original. The only possible happy outcome is an oncoming bow caught before serious damage occurs.

 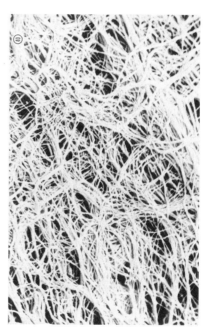

NORMAL   SCARRED

On the left, we see the normal arrangement of tendon fibers in line with smaller, mature crosslinks between them. On the right are randomly organized collagen fibers in scar tissue at four months after injury.

(Photographs courtesy of Dr. Ian Silver[1] and Dr. Peter Rossdale)

Don't be fooled by a perfect-looking ex-bowed tendon. A bump may remain on a healed tendon forever, caused by pockets of scar tissue and cell debris that have been encapsulated within the healing tendon. On the other hand, partially healed tendons may look perfectly normal to the naked eye. If you put both of these horses back into heavy work, it will be the "normal" tendon that will rebow.

---

1. Dr. Ian Silver, Dr. Peter Rossdale, et al, *A clinical and experimental study of tendon injury, healing and treatment in the horse*, University of Bristol, supplement to The Equine Veterinary Journal (July, 1983).

Chapter 8: Treating The Bowed Tendon

Time counts! Immediately after a bow occurs, we face a situation where dilated and broken blood vessels are pouring fluids and blood cells into the injured area. Your attention must be focused on controlling the heat and swelling which are body's immune reaction to the damage. Heat and swelling are the outward result but, internally, extra damage is being done while the condition exists. Your horse's future may depend on the actions you take in the first few hours after the injury.

The most appropriate treatment for the specific bow your horse has suffered is best prescribed by your veterinarian. What follows here is a discussion of the most likely treatments and therapies available, as well as a discussion of decisions you will be required to make regarding such treatment.

First, a timetable of events, starting within a few minutes of discovering heat and swelling in or near a tendon:

In the first hour:

1. Confine the horse and keep him calm.
2. Apply ice or cryotherapy.
3. Call your veterinarian.
4. Give anti-inflammatories as vet recommends.

During the first 24-48 Hours:

1. Continue cryotherapy, icing every 4 hours.
2. Continue with medications and other treatments recommended by veterinarian (poultices, etc.).
3. Cut feed intake to maintenance levels.
4. Keep the animal confined and calm.
5. Get an ultrasound scan done of the injured area.

Once swelling is under control (approx. 72 hours):

1. Begin alternating hot and cold treatments as outlined below. Twice a day, each.
2. Cut back on anti-inflammatories.
3. Keep horse in a quiet, calm environment.

At two weeks:

1. Begin therapies and therapeutics that you and your vet deem worthwhile (see choices below).

2. You can take the horse out of the stall and walk him. This is not therapeutic exercise - just enough to estimate the pain he's experiencing and let his joints flex a little.

3. Use hot treatments before exercise, cold treatments after. Once a day if swelling, heat and pain are under control.

4. No turn outs, no excitement.

At one month:

1. Take another ultrasound scan, looking for any remaining pockets of fluid.

2. If the horse is not lame and healing is definitely underway, begin light walking exercise, gradually increasing the distance of the walk - making sure to keep the horse relaxed and under control.

3. Continue hot/cold treatments.

4. Focus therapies on fluid-filled areas.

At 90 days:

1. Another Ultrasound scan, this one to determine extent of healing.

2. If healing is taking place, increase exercise load to a weight-bearing walk, later trot.

3. Continue once a day hot/cold treatments.

At 6 months:

1. Another ultrasound scan. Hopefully, there will be no sign of "holes" in the tendon at this point.

2. Begin conditioning your athlete as if it was going through the training program for the first time, beginning with Long Slow Distance.

3. Continue hot/cold treatments and therapies. You should be off all drugs by this point.

4. If all the signs are good, you can start turning the horse out into a small paddock - after controlled exercise.

5. Increase ration to support workload.

6. Use cold therapy after work every day.

From here on, it's a matter of slowly rebuilding your athlete while maintaining control over his daily activities. Continue with cold therapy after exercise, and continue with regular ultrasound scans. While you will not be able to see any improvements if the tendon remains stable, you'll see the beginnings of signs that your exercise load is too heavy, long before you rebow the horse.

Now, let's look more deeply into the whys and hows of bowed tendon treatments, from the very minute you recognize you have a problem.

First Aid: Within minutes of the very first indications of tendon damage ice should be applied to control heat and swelling and thus to limit their damaging effects. This is called cryotherapy and it demands ice. Not cold water, but ice. Cold water just doesn't have enough cooling power to close the vasculature, or blood vessels, and restrict swelling. Cryotherapy or cold therapy, in the form of ice, tends to cause the vasculature to contract, limiting damaging inflammation. Cryotherapy is the very best first aid a bowed tendon can receive.

Ice is a far better approach than cold water or frozen wraps, and an ice cube maker is a vital tool for a large stable. If you don't have an ice cube maker then get some ice cubes out of the refrigerator and crush them. You need enough ice to fill the bottom two or three inches of the bucket. Fill the bucket 2/3 of the way up with water, and then add alcohol to fill the bucket. The ratio of water to alcohol is 2:1. Alcohol will lower the temperature of the water you'll be applying to the bow.

Drop two polo bandages into the bucket and swish them around so they are wetted thoroughly. Starting at the fetlock, wrap the injured area loosely, pulling small pockets or gaps into each overlap of the bandage. Apply the second polo in the same way, starting mid-cannon and continuing up over the knee. Pour the ice water/ alcohol mix over the leg and into the little pockets you made when wrapping the bandage. Keep this up for about 20 minutes at a time. Repeat this every 4 hours around the clock for the first 24 hours - this is the critical period when a lot of additional damage can be done. Continue the process at least 4 times a day until the leg's swelling and heat has subsided significantly (usually about 72 hours).

Confine the horse to a quiet stall. The horse needs complete stall rest, from a few days for a mild strain to several weeks for a severe bow. If the horse's normal stall is in a busy area, move him. He needs to stand quietly, not run to the door and stick his head out at passersby.

Cryotherapy:

Studies of a variety of cryotherapy modes suggest that circulating ice water flowing over the affected area is the most effective treatment. Other modes, such as frozen ice packs and applied refrigeration coils are less effective. This is because a local equalization effect quickly takes place between the tissue and the adjacent cold device. Circulating ice water ensures that a continuous flowing source of cold is always present. Standing the horse in a muck bucket full of ice water will cool the leg, but it will also soak the hoof as well. (A hoof that is repeatedly saturated with water actually loses moisture and dries out.) And pouring ice water into polo bandages is no more of a mess and yards safer than an overturned muck bucket.

There is a danger in applying effective cold therapy for too long a period of time. When tissues reach 15 degrees Centigrade, the body concludes the parts are about to freeze and floods the area with warm blood - just the opposite of what we want. This is called the Hunter reaction. In humans, it occurs after about 20 minutes of circulating ice water application. To be safe, then, ice water should be applied to a bowed tendon for 20 minutes at a time every 4 hours.

Icing also has an analgesic, or pain killing, effect. A horse with a sore tendon may not be nearly as sore after icing, and if you turn the animal out into a paddock after treatment, it's liable to overdo its activity under the false assumption that the tendon is suddenly better. This analgesic effect can last as long as four hours, even if the horse is warmed up and sweating, with no cold remaining in the tendon at all. Endorphins are circulating, and those are the pain killers.

Call the vet - preferably one with an ultrasound imaging machine. In the case of a severe bow, Banamine or another anti-inflammatory (Butazolidin is another choice) should be given immediately to reduce the swelling. You want to avoid a long delay before administering the drug - time counts in this case, but it is important that you've discussed with your vet exactly what to do in the case of an oncoming bow. He may direct you to administer

74

an anti-inflammatory such as Bute or Banamine, before he arrives, so it is best if you have already set up a first aid kit with the help of your vet - one that includes anti-inflammatories and instructions on their use in emergencies.

Anti-inflammatory drugs may be needed for only a few days if the injury is mild. Serious tendon damage will require more prolonged drug therapy, for several days to a few weeks to control the pain and swelling.

The Emergency Kit:

The stable should always have an emergency first aid kit on hand. Your vet can help you put one together. As far as bowed tendons are concerned, you need the following:

✓ At least two clean, fuzzy polo bandages.
✓ An immediate source of ice.
✓ Several quarts of alcohol.
✓ An anti-inflammatory drug like Banamine.
✓ A tranquilizer like Acepromazine.

As the vet examines the horse, tell him/her at what time you noticed the condition, what measures you have taken, what the horse's workload and shoeing schedule have been and any other pertinent details. The vet will take ultrasound pictures of the leg to determine the true extent of the damage. The initial ultrasound scan establishes a benchmark for the damage. Future ultrasounds will be compared to that benchmark to determine how the healing process is progressing.

Reduce the rations: It goes without saying that the rations should be cut, for lots of reasons, including the possibility that the horse will tie up. Ask the veterinarian if the pain killing medication should be cut back if the animal is too frisky. If the horse is acting up and is in danger of aggravating the injury, a tranquilizer becomes appropriate. In a very fit animal, you may find it necessary to tranquilize the horse for a time. Part of the result of icing the leg is that you reduce pain and swelling. A fit horse is going to have energy to burn and he's going to feel very little pain in his injured tendon after icing. So, he'll want to fool around. You can't allow that.

Diagnostic Ultrasound:

Ultrasound scanning is a diagnostic tool that allows the equivalent of x-rays to be taken of soft tissue. The machine sends sound into the tissue and records the echoes in order to display an image of soft tissue structures. Healthy tissue shows as regular gray-to-white patterns on the ultrasound monitor. Damaged areas of tendons and ligaments appear irregular and "ratty", with black spots that represent tears in the tendon. Tears fill with blood and fluid that do not return the sound - hence, no echoes.

What you'll be looking for is a gradual shrinkage of the black pockets of fluid that initially showed the extent of the tendon injury. Once these disappear, you'll want to see a regularity to the actual fiber structure itself, with no mottling of the echograph. Even when it appears that all the holes are plugged and the fibers properly aligned, remember that this new collagen is likely to be mostly composed of immature Type II and Type III fibers.

During the process of rehab, the only way to be sure that the tendon is healing is to periodically examine it though ultrasound sector scanning, using a practitioner who knows what he's looking at when he uses the machine. There aren't many of these in practice at present, but expertise is growing and papers and books are being introduced that will allow you to follow your horse's progress.

I'd suggest a new ultrasound scan every 30 days. Every 60 days is the absolute minimum. And another 120 days of progressively loaded exercise that gradually approaches former stress levels - after everything seems absolutely perfect on the ultrasound monitor. Even then, if you go back to the same exercise loads and mechanical conditions that initially caused the bow, the odds are that you'll eventually have a recurrence.

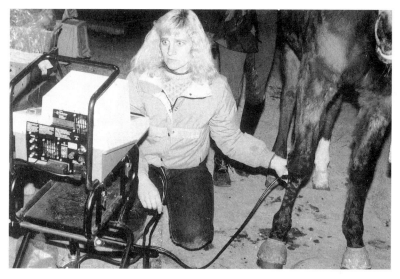

Dr. Carla Burno (Willow Creek Equine Clinic) performs an ultrasound exam. *(Photo by Judy Hanson)*

Ice alternating with heat: Seventy two hours following the injury, cold therapy is no longer effective by itself. Anti-inflammatory drugs are taking over the job and there is need for periodic increased circulation through the injured area to move clotted blood and tissue debris away. That's when hot applications begin to be useful. Heat increases local circulation.

On the one hand, increased circulation means the likelihood of increased swelling immediately. But damaged cells and other debris and poisons must be removed from the area as healing gets underway, or pain and swelling - a whole spectrum of immune system overreactions - can continue far longer than necessary. Heat opens blood vessels and allows waste products and coagulated blood to be carried out of the area. Following heat application by cold closes the blood vessels again, inhibiting further inflammation. This will speed healing and help prevent adhesions or non-healing pockets of blood and debris.

Within 72 hours, the tendon swelling should be under control enough to begin alternating hot/cold treatments. Heat is applied in the same manner as cold. Soak two polo bandages in very warm water (as hot as you can keep your hand in - less than 120 degrees), then wrap the leg and pour cups of the warm water into the folds of the bandage. Another method is to slather the leg with glycerin, cover it with plastic wrap and apply a standing bandage. A mixture of DMSO and furacin can be used in the same manner.

The duration of treatment is not critical. Heat can be applied less aggressively and for longer periods than cold, as long as swelling is not aggravated. Warm to semi-hot water wraps can be used for a few minutes while glycerin wraps that rely on body temperature as a source of heat can be left on longer, even overnight. Ice the leg after each heat treatment.

Another effective delivery method for heat is ultrasound therapy, administered by a vet or a therapist. Alternating hot/cold treatments are useful in the beginning, and ultrasound therapy can help all through the healing process, once inflammation is under control. Ultrasound therapy is not the same thing as ultrasound scanning, which is a diagnostic tool. Ultrasound therapy is a matter of sending ultrasound into tissues at a certain intensity and frequency. The sound jiggles the organic molecules and produces heat deep within them - much like a microwave oven works, except that ultrasound devices are not strong enough to "cook" your horse. The internal heat produced by ultrasound treatment encourages circulation to and from the areas being treated and thus promotes healing.

Using an ultrasound device effectively and safely requires expertise. You can cause more injury than you heal with improper use of ultrasound, so hire an expert. One well known therapist is Mimi Porter of Lexington, Ky (606) 223-1326.

So the most effective practice, once swelling has been brought under control, is to open up circulation for a time with heat or ultrasound, then tighten down again with cold therapy. Always follow heat, ultrasound or sweat treatments with icing.

Raising hoof angles: Elevating both heels (which raises the hoof angles) during these initial stages can help prevent further injury if you're dealing with a deep flexor tendon injury, but has no effect on a superficial flexor tendon injury. The angles are raised no more than two degrees at one time. If the horse has decent hoof angles to start with, the change will be slight and can be accomplished with trimming. But if the horse has been wearing long toes and low heels, the farrier must apply degree pads to the shoes. Every three to four weeks, the heels can be raised another 2 degrees, until the hooves have a normal angle. If the horse had a 44 degree hoof, it may take four such resets to achieve the proper angle.

Casts, splints and braces are not for a common bow, but a ruptured tendon may require a cast or a brace. Your vet will apply the cast and remove it when the time comes.

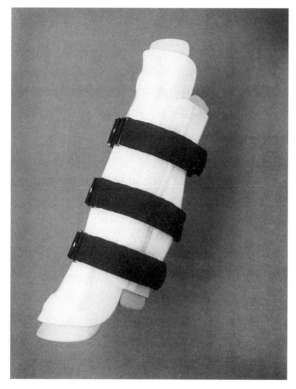

The Farley Splint is one of the best-known and most successfully used splints for severe tendon tears.

(Photo courtesy of Equine Orthotics, Inc.)

Within six hours of the injury, and up to six weeks thereafter, placing the injured limb in an immobilization cast seems to speed initial injury repair. Once healing is seriously underway, though, light flexing exercise can help align forming collagen fibers in the appropriate direction of stress while helping to prevent adhesions. So, at some point, the cast is removed and the animal is gradually introduced to fetlock-flexing exercises, beginning with a slow walk.

Follow-up Ultrasounds: The vet will want to do a second ultrasound exam in two weeks to one month after the initial injury. He needs to know much healing has taken place through the various forms of therapy before any real exercise therapy begins. Thereafter, monthly ultrasound exams for the first three to four months is money well spent. The more you stay on top of the situation, the sooner you can think about exercise therapy, which is rehabilitation.

Wraps: During this early period of recovery, you may be tempted to wrap both front legs, just to "help the horse out" and to "give him a little extra support." Don't. The horse that is resting in his stall or walking in the light stages of rehab will not bow the good leg from standing on the bad one. Out of 100 bowed tendons, 99 need no special support. (The last one is a ruptured tendon and belongs in an equine veterinary hospital, where you can't fool with it.) If you still want to wrap the legs, read the section on Coverups later in this chapter.

Corticosteroids: During the initial exam, you may be faced with the question of whether to administer corticosteroids. In 99 cases out of 100, using corticosteroids is a mistake. (See Chapter 10 for more information.)

Coverups: All the old-timers you'll meet will have their favorite non-vet remedies for "doctoring" a tendon. Most of these are aimed at getting the area "tight". This can be fine during the first few days after a fresh bow occurs, because too much swelling, as explained above, will cause further damage to the tendon. But once the severe heat and swelling have settled down, the normal healing process is going to involve some edema in the area. Has to. The serum-like fluids are there to transport healing materials in and cell debris out.

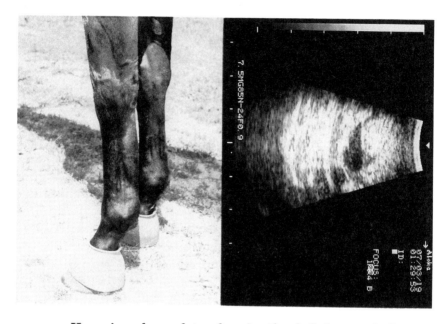

Here is a bowed tendon in the left leg and the ultrasound of that bow. This middle bow doesn't bulge outward as much as the usual torn superficial digital flexor tendon. Most of the swelling is between the tendons.

Reading the ultrasound scan: the white band at the right is the skin, followed inward by a white circle that is the superficial flexor tendon. The large, dark area is a pocket of blood, now probably scar tissue. The lower portion of this pocket "bleeds into" the superficial flexor tendon, where the tendon has ruptured. The second dark spot of fluid, farther to the left, may indicate deep digital flexor tendon involvement. The swelling in this leg never went away - the leg looks this bad today, showing the kind of severe damage you get from uncontrolled swelling. This horse will never see the racetrack again.

There is very little scientific information available on the use of liniments, astringents, poultices, rubs or wraps in the treatment of a bow, but here are some thoughts. Liniments of the normal kind, i.e. wintergreen or foul-smelling "coolants" tend to ease little aches and pains and do very little otherwise. DMSO is a topical anti-inflammatory and can be used to help reduce swelling. However, DMSO will carry other chemicals into the flesh, and if you're using a liniment or treatment that will be irritating if it gets under the skin, then DMSO should be avoided.

There are irritant rubs and blistering rubs, but these act on the outer skin, not on the underlying tendon. They'll tend to make the skin tougher, like leather, but will not do anything for underlying structures. One popular quack remedy is made of crushed orange peels, providing some local anaesthetic and probably enough irritation to cause some tightening of the skin. No cure, though. Just a magic trick. And any liniment, sweat, rub or sauce, if applied with enough enthusiasm, can irritate the skin and underlying tissues enough cause widespread inflammation, even infection. Then, more damage will occur. However, there is no known topical substance that promotes healing.

A poultice is used to draw fluids from the tissues that come in contact with it. Poulticing an infected foot can be effective because it'll aid in drawing the infection out at the coronary band or, sometimes, through the bottom of the hoof. Poultices act more like DMSO, in that they tend to reduce swelling. Poulticing a bow will tend to make the tendon look prettier because it reduces the amount of fluid surrounding the injury. But this artificial "tightness" says absolutely nothing about the condition of the tendon underneath the skin. In fact, the "normalizing" of the tendon invariably leads to the next deadly mistake: going on with an injured horse.

Sweat bandages have a similar effect, as do wraps using DMSO mixed with other potions, notably corticosteroids. They're all great coverups, just in case the owner decides to visit and you haven't told him about the bow yet. They can be used to control filling and edema, but they have little or no effect on the healing process and, in some cases, may result in further injury.

For example, attempts to "tighten" a bow with tight

wraps or support bandages may result in a constriction that cuts off the blood supply to the injured area or areas nearby. Remember, there is swelling from the inside, so constricting from the outside puts living tissues "between a rock and a hard place".

In short, there is nothing you can put on the outside of a bowed tendon that will help it heal. You can make the tendon look prettier, and feel better, but you cannot heal a tendon from the outside. Aside from limiting the initial immune reaction - heat and swelling - by applying ice, there is nothing you can do with topical applicants and bandages to speed healing. But there are many things you can do to fool yourself, and the horse, into believing that the tendon is all better and ready for more punishment.

Tincture of Time

There are no miracles available in the healing of a bowed tendon. More often than not, if you try for a miracle treatment that will bring your horse back in half the time normally required, you're going to be sadly disappointed in the ultimate results. You'll have a worse situation than you had to begin with, and you'll have lost time and money in the process.

Your goal should be complete healing, not bringing the horse back quick enough for fall competition. With that principle in mind, it should be an easy matter to decide on the procedures you want to use to rehabilitate your horse. If you have a good vet, and point out your goal very clearly, you'll get good advice and help when you need it. But don't let the vet tell you what he thinks you want to hear, and don't ask him to violate his own hard-learned medical principles. "Help me heal the horse, Doc."

Meanwhile, you have to pay attention to detail throughout the healing process. You have to think ahead about the consequences of an action before taking it. For example, when to begin therapeutic exercise and how fast to progress with it. Or when to turn the animal out into a large paddock. It should be blatantly obvious that, if you're unwilling to train the horse at 40 MPH for fear you'll reinjure the tendon, then turning out the animal into a large paddock, where he just might feel like having a little fun at 40 MPH after being cooped up for a while, is probably a horrendous mistake.

The most important detail, of course, is knowing exactly what the status of the tendon is from week to week, month to month. If your animal is valuable, and you're anxious to bring him back to former performance levels, then there is no substitute for frequent ultrasound examinations to see exactly how far along the healing process has come. If returning to competition is less of a concern, then the cost of frequent scans can be avoided - just give the horse more than enough time to completely heal. Remember, outward appearances can be very deceiving along about 90 to 120 days into the healing process. Above all, focus on limiting the extent of the initial injury by noticing it early, acting quickly with first aid and veterinary help, and avoiding further stressing of the injured part.

Chapter 9: Firing and Blistering

The tradition of equine husbandry and veterinary medicine includes the old saw, "fight fire with fire." That is, if an injured area is hot and swollen, burn it into submission. The underlying "scientific" concept is that burning causes increased circulation to the affected area, and with it, a quicker, more effective, healing response. Modern science says that increased heat and swelling does more damage to the injured area and actually restricts circulation and healing. Still, the practices of firing and blistering continue unabated. Only when veterinarians are forced to submit to firing and blistering themselves as a cure for their aches and pains, will the barbaric but lucrative practice be curtailed.

Firing, or cautery, is the insertion of a red-hot iron into the skin over the tendon area, resulting in burning of the flesh. The firing iron may be used only on the skin or it may be inserted directly into the tendons. Afterwards, the skin on the horse's leg looks just like yours would if someone burned you with a cherry-red poker. Feels about the same, too.

All sorts of artistic designs are used in firing, including line firing, pin firing, and bar firing. Line firing sears the flesh in a line while pin firing shotguns little points of burns all over the injured area. Bar firing uses an elongated hot bar to save time, branding the horse with a series of stripes up and down the tendon. There are theories about which firing pattern affords the most healing benefits, but the single answer is: none of them. The firing of a bowed tendon heals only the veterinarian's pocketbook.

Firing is often followed by blistering. Blistering is applying an irritant or caustic solution to the skin. An substance such as mercuric iodine, a volatile oil such as turpentine or mustard oil, or a strong solution of ammonia is applied, usually with a paintbrush, and the leg is wrapped to maximize the effectiveness of the irritant. Redness, swelling, severe irritation and inflammation culminating in the formation of blisters are considered the "therapeutic" stages of blistering.

The result of both firing and blistering is pain, swelling and blisters. Pustulation is a common consequence. Pustulation is blisters filled with pus, a condition which often leads to the death and sloughing of the skin and underlying tissues, including damage to the deeper layers of skin, to the tendons or to the joint. The horse must usually be physically restrained to prevent self-mutilation, as he tries to chew at the source of his agony. These modalities are often used together as a way of getting circulation to an injured body part - or as a cynical way for a veterinarian to enforce his prescription of rest.

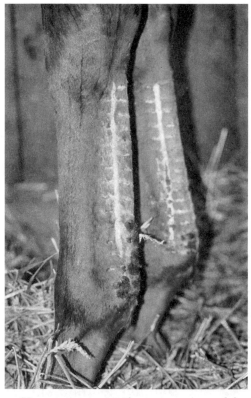

An example of line or bar firing. Note how the straw sticks to the still-oozing scabs.
(Photograph courtesy of Suzie Oldham)

You may question my own objectivity when it comes to firing and blistering, since I call those practitioners who use the technique "quacks". Rightfully so. I confess a distinct prejudice against firing and blistering that was seared into my brain early in my training career. I was stabled next to an area where a vet/professor from one of our prestigious universities was instructing students - they were on the opposite side of the shedrow and the vet was talking about how firing may do no good, but it was a money-maker and at least kept the injured horse off the racetrack for a while. Then he demonstrated the technique.

After the vet and his students had left for the day, and after the local anaesthetic had worn off, the treated horse began to scream. He screamed and moaned for 48 hours straight, until he was led away due to complaints from all of the rest of us located anywhere near that stall. In frontier days, when justice was often uncomplicated and swift, and where horses were far more important than they are today, this medicine man would have quickly received a .45 slug to the brain from any of a dozen different directions. Today's society is a little more primitive, as far as horses are concerned.

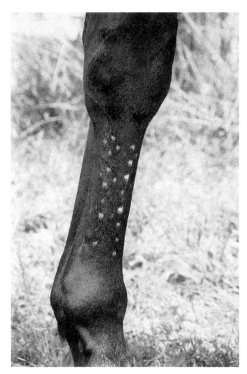

A pin fired leg with a windpuff in the middle.
(Photograph by Suzie Oldham)

Veterinarians, our Medicine Men, have a responsibility to their equine patients much like medical doctors - they've sworn that their patients will receive ethical care. But money rules the conscience of many of these charlatans, especially those practicing at the racetrack. Much of the equine medicine practiced at the racetrack, is little more than 16th century dentistry with rampant drug misuse thrown in. Even your friendly country practitioner has his or her faults.

For most vets, diagnostics is a waste of time - nobody pays for diagnostics, just the coverup drugs or quack treatments. Most medical doctors must keep up with new developments in their areas of practice - by law. There is little evidence that many old-time vets can read, much less keep up with modern technology. If your veterinarian still fires and blisters horses, he's one of these, no matter his age.

Veterinary medicine ignores the developments in human medicine except for drug technology. This club of practitioners knows where its bread is buttered and, rather than promote truth, preventative medicine and the welfare of the horse, they cause more injuries than they cure and charge outrageously for treatments they know, for certain, will do more damage than the original injury. All for money. They're like lawyers - too damn many of them.

Not all. I've met dozens of vets who attempt to swim upriver and do the right thing. They're ostracized by their peers and by the trainers they serve. Why the trainers? Because trainers don't read either, and they believe that coverup drugs and false hopes will bring in a few more dollars before the owner must be told the truth. They pretend to be doing "everything humanly possible" for the horse while sucking the owner dry - it's a great partnership. There are good vets out there, but they have a hard time surviving.

At any rate, the possible negative consequences of firing and blistering are many, from infection, sloughing skin, severely damaged tendons and periosteums, to founder and disfigurement - all for no worthwhile result except to transfer funds from owners' bank accounts. As Dr. Baxter Black says, the motto of most veterinary schools is written in Latin so few laymen can understand it. Here's a translation: "No matter how hard you try, you can't kill 'em all."

From 1977 through 1981 a study of ruptured tendons

and treatments was conducted in England, resulting in a paper[1]. It is thought that this study weighed in heavily toward the banning of firing as a medical treatment in Europe. The paper concluded:

"Pathological studies showed that tendon healing is a very prolonged process and continues after 15 months. Firing did not alter this process except in the case of pin firing, where injury to the actual tendon prolonged the healing and resulted in further damage. Scar collagen in pin fired tendons did not align along lines of stress and remained as cores of permanent weakness. Fired skin, after an initial period of acute inflammation and oedema, produced local areas which were thinner and weaker than normal skin."

Pin firing. The smell of burning flesh, once experienced, is never forgotten. *(Photograph by Louise Reinagel)*

---

[1] Dr. Ian Silver, Dr. Peter Rossdale, et al, *A clinical and experimental study of tendon injury, healing and treatment in the horse.* University of Bristol, supplement to The Equine Veterinary Journal (July, 1983).

Chapter 10: Corticosteroids

Corticosteroids are extremely potent anti-inflammatories used to control rampant swelling. More often than not, corticosteroids are used as a coverup medication in order to keep an injured horse in competition. It is this "normalizing" use of these chemicals which causes far more damage than it alleviates. Here's why:

Corticosteroids don't heal the damaged tendon, they mask the damage, and quite effectively. The edema and heat will be swept away almost overnight. But all an injection of Dexamethasone, or any other corticosteroid, does is to make a tendon *look* pretty. In fact, that pretty "brand new" tendon, and the tissues around it, are going to be weakened considerably by the corticosteroid. If you use a topical ointment that contains a corticosteroid, especially one mixed with DMSO, something similar will happen. It'll look like you've effected a cure, and there are some vets who will profess to have solved your tendon problem. Quacks. There are other possible problems with corticosteroids, including suppression of the immune system, infection, and founder. Bad news except for the most acute problems involving inflammation.

Corticosteriods are the counterfeit aircraft engine parts of the horse business. They'll reduce the swelling and make that tendon look pretty - so that you can perhaps sell the horse to an unsuspecting buyer, or persuade a state vet to allow the horse into Saturday's race. Autopsies of many racehorses have shown that corticosteroid injections into tendon tissue cause the formation of bone cells within the tendon, making it stiff, less flexible, and causing not only bowed tendons but sesamoid injury as well. It is moronic and unethical to use corticosteroids as a way to return the horse to competition.

Corticosteroids encourage catabolism (protein breakdown) and discourage anabolism (protein building), hampering healing substantially. The only time a corticosteroid injection is at all useful with a bow is when the swelling is so severe that a lot of additional damage is likely if the edema is left to its natural resolution and you are making a last ditch effort to control severe swelling. In this case, it's best to use them systemically (intramuscularly or sometimes intravenously), not injected right into the tendon. But realize you have a severely injured horse which is going to require more than a year to heal - and the corticosteroid will delay that healing further.

There are no shortcuts. Take the high road and heal the horse. Otherwise, you're liable to find yourself in a situation similar to this:

At 5:40 P.M., June 5, 1993, a 3-year-old thoroughbred chestnut gelding, lip tattoo T 21905, broke down on the backstretch of Belmont Park and was humanely destroyed. At 5:50 A. M., June 6, a necropsy was performed at Cornell University by Dr. Lennart Krook, pathologist, Dr. Eric Blomme, resident, and student-on-duty, Leah Goodman.

Prairie Bayou was the favorite for the Belmont Stakes. He was owned by John Ed Anthony's Loblolly Stable and was a strong winner in the Preakness Stakes a few weeks earlier. The horse looked fine in the saddling paddock and during the post parade. But halfway through the 1 1/2 mile race, in no real traffic, traveling at a moderate pace as the race was setting up along the backstretch, the horse broke down and had to be destroyed, joining the ranks of lost Thoroughbred heroes like Go For Wand, Ruffian and another 800 or so lesser lights who die before racing fans each year. Many more die out of sight and out of the minds of the viewing public.

The following appeared in the "comments" section of the necropsy report on Prairie Bayou prepared by Dr. Lennart Krook of Cornell University:

"The most important microscopic finding is the severe degeneration and necrosis of the medial branch of the suspensory ligament close to its attachment to the top of the medial sesamoid bone of the left front leg. Similar but minor changes were observed in the lateral branch. The branches of the suspensory ligaments away from the sesamoid bones, the distal sesamoidean ligaments and the superficial and deep digital flexor tendons showed no significant changes. The lesions of the suspensory ligament next to the sesamoid

bones are, thus, localized. It would be reasonable to conclude that these parts were exposed to a toxic agent. (Emphasis added.)

"The degeneration and necrosis of the medial branch of the suspensory ligament, left front, obviously compromised the normal function of this ligament. It is my considered conclusion that this was the cause of the fracture of the medial sesamoid bone. The other fractures, that of the lateral condyle of the cannon bone and that of the long pastern bone, are considered immediate consequences secondary to the sesamoid bone fracture.

"With emphasis of the damage to the suspensory ligament, the fractures are considered pathologic."

What Dr. Krook is saying is that a "toxic agent" destroyed the suspensory ligament and that the multiple fractures were a result.

In his book, Race Horses At Risk[1] , Dr. Krook expands upon how toxic agents are introduced into the ligaments and tendons of racehorses: "Chondro-osteo-necrosis and tendon degeneration are caused by injection of corticosteroids into joints and tendons."

He gives an example, a filly with chips in her knees: "These chips in the knees caused lameness on which the filly could not run. There was swelling and pain of the knee, both signs of an inflammation. The filly became a "basket case" with very little chance of future success. The affected knee was injected with corticosteroids (Depo-Medrol) 3 times over 70 days, the last time 2 days before a cheap claiming race. Shortly after the start, she fractured the cannon bone. The filly fell into two oncoming horses, which fell on their necks and were destroyed, as was the filly. Riding one of the horses was a jockey who sustained severe head injuries and became incapacitated for life.

"This scenario, with a fatal outcome to the horse but not the jockey, is often repeated in thoroughbred races. Osteochondrosis is a very common affliction of race horses that can and does cause chips in various joints. This sets up an inflammatory reaction, a cardinal sign of which is pain. This pain tells the horse not to run on an inflamed tendon or ligament or a joint. A horse cannot and should not train or race with any of these conditions. Then, however, corticosteroids are injected. They are powerful anti-inflammatory agents and, by blocking varying enzymes involved in the inflammatory process, extinguish the signs of inflammation, including pain. The horse is then led to the parade where it is declared racing sound because the signs of inflammation have been canceled by an injection of a disease-inducing drug.

"We have quoted above from Sweetnam: 'Certainly no such injection should be given to an athlete without adequate explanation of the risk involved.' The risk involved is not explained to the horse, which is not treated as an athlete but as a running machine expected to run just another race at the risk of his/her life. Nor is it explained to the horse's jockey, or to the jockeys of other horses, all of whom run an increased risk of being injured by the fall of a horse treated with corticosteroids."

And that's the way it was, according to the reasonable conclusions of an autopsy, when Prairie Bayou failed to win the Belmont. Prairie Bayou's owners vehemently deny that their horse was ever injected with corticosteroids. Their statement is undoubtedly made in good faith. But a racehorse passes through so many handlers throughout a racing career that it is unlikely any owner ever knows the full extent of medication administered to his or her horses. For example, a hyaluronic acid injection, used to treat an ankle joint, generally contains a corticosteroid to prevent an inflammatory reaction. The owner's vet bill would not mention the corticosteroid. Then, too, there is nothing illegal or, by racing standards, even immoral in using corticosteroids.

What is encouraging about the Prairie Bayou incident is the owner's adamant position that his stable does not condone the use of corticosteroids. Loblolly Stable recognizes the insidious damage caused by such drugs. What is distressing, however, is the length to which some of the racing industry's leaders have gone to discredit Dr. Krook's findings and research.

---

[1] Dr. Lennart Krook and Dr. George A. Maylin, *Race Horses at Risk*, published by the authors, 1989 (Ithaca, N.Y.) pp. 194-196.

Chapter 11: Exotic Treatments

In the movies, the wounded soldier yells "Medic!" and an amateur medicine man runs up with bandages and morphine to patch the warrior up. With that accomplished, the soldier returns to the fray. We pretend it's the same with our particular brand of cannon fodder, the performance horse. We yell "Medic," the vet comes in with his satchel full of needles and patches up our animal for Saturday's competition. At least, that's what we'd like to believe will happen. And the vets have some fairly brilliant tricks that make it appear that they've actually performed such a miracle.

I'm going to begin this chapter by telling you point blank that a full-blown bowed tendon, that is, one that you can see from a few feet away, means the end of your horse's present athletic career in most cases, no matter how much money you spend on miracle cures. There are no manmade cures, and the completely healed ruptured tendon is a major project even for Mother Nature. That's why the ads for this book encourage you to buy it **before** your horse incurs a bow.

In this chapter, I'm going to look at some of the more exotic healing modalities for ruptured tendons, one at a time. They range from conceivably helpful to moronic. Bear in mind that no treatment has even approached the efficacy of ice, rest and rehab through exercise therapy.

Tendon Splitting

This concept is based upon increasing the repair activity in the healing tendon. In this case, multiple lacerations are cut into the tendon near the injured site, with hopes that the animal's immune system will respond that much more vehemently and repair all the damage quickly and completely. Nope. Professor Silver established the uselessness of tendon splitting in his paper entitled *A clinical and experimental study of tendon injury, healing, and treatment in the horse.* Again, from I. A. Silver, et al:

"A slender stillette type knife was introduced and run distally through the injured tendon into the adjacent normal tissue. The knife was then withdrawn and reintroduced to run proximally in normal tissue towards the carpus, the "splitting" being in the central region of the tendon thickness. Following "splitting", the incision was closed with a single suture of monofilament nylon.

"The tendon split groups showed a uniform decrease in performance as compared to untreated controls at 8, 11, and 14 months after treatment. On the basis of these observations we have to conclude that line firing is not an effective treatment for acute or chronic injury and that pin firing and tendon splitting are detrimental."

The problem is this: any damage to the tendon promotes the proliferation of Type III collagen. Type III collagen is immature collagen, usually found in blood vessels and digestive tract structures. It is quite elastic, but does not have the tensile strength of mature Type I collagen. Inflicting further damage on the tendon simply increases the Type III collagen content of the tendon. To the extent that you encourage the development of Type III collagen, you're compromising the full healing of the tendon. The scarring that comes with tendon splitting is like that from pin firing. It contains Type III collagen and it remains within the tendon for a very long time, well beyond 14 months. Meanwhile, the extra disruption caused by tendon splitting or pin firing inhibits the overall production of collagen by as much as 20%.

In addition, these aggressive attempts at tendon healing promote adhesions between the tendons and their sheaths. During the healing process, the adhesions must be broken, or the tendons will lose their normal flexibility. With high stress, adhesions will break anyway, but heat and swelling will return, again and again, to haunt the trainer and his animal. No fun in the best of circumstances.

Carbon Implants

In cases of severely injured and even severed tendons, carbon fibers, like those used in building helicopter rotor blades and airplane wings, can be sutured into the remaining viable tendon tissue to stabilize the tendon and allow for some weight bearing. Over time, new tendon collagen fibers will regenerate and they'll follow along the carbon fibers, in line with stress. Eventually, with the carbon surrounded by new tendon collagen, the carbon fibers dissolve, leaving a reasonably strong new tendon behind.

I've seen total replacement of the middle portion of a superficial flexor tendon in an Australian Standardbred lead to a horse with a very fat leg that could race and win again. However, this is an extremely invasive surgical technique and large amounts of scar tissue form that will never become tendon tissue. Carbon implants are for simply keeping a severely injured but valuable horse alive and viable for breeding purposes or light exercise. The athlete is finished as far as high intensity performances are concerned. Still, for a horse with breeding potential, or one you want to save for any reason, this technique can work a miracle on a horse that would otherwise have to be put down.

Superior Check Ligament Desmotomy.

The superior check ligament "checks" the participation of the flexor muscles in the absorption of stretching forces in the lower leg. Cutting the superior check ligament allows the muscles to "help" the injured tendon absorb some of these stresses. The theory is that the healed tendon, even though it's weaker than the original tendon, may just survive high stress with the help of the flexor muscles. This does not help the injured tendon heal - it simply reduces the stretching forces somewhat.

I'm doubtful about this new technique, at least as far as complete rehabilitation is concerned. I'm afraid it may become another veterinary fad. While this does allow the flexor muscles to take on more of the stretching duties from the flexor tendons, I'm personally wary because I've already seen Thoroughbreds rebowing after such an operation. The success of this strategy depends almost entirely on the degree of damage in the tendon. Severe injuries, or improperly healed injuries, can't get enough benefit from the flexor muscles to overcome their inherent weaknesses. However, Dr. Larry Bramlage, of Lexington, Ky, claims that his experience indicates many horses can return to strenuous activity, including racing. If you are desperate, try this technique and then let me know how it works for you. You can reach me at (812) 427-3305, or call my publisher, Russell Meerdink for an updated phone number.

The superior check ligament is there for a reason. Probably for a number of reasons. The old saying is, "If the surgery leaves a part of the horse on the table, his chances for full recovery are reduced." Besides, if you're going to start chopping away at the functional anatomy of the horse, why not take the leg off at the knee and attach a nice set of Goodyear Eagles - solve the whole tendon problem at once!

Annular Ligament Desmotomy

As you know from earlier chapters, the annular ligament wraps around the fetlock, holding a number of structures in place. When injury occurs in the fetlock, especially soft tissue injury, the resulting swelling threatens the flexor tendons with damage or additional damage as well as severely reduced circulation. Annular ligament desmotomy means resecting, or cutting through the main body of this broad ligament, starting at the top and cutting down to just under the fetlock. Sometimes, where chronic inflammation has "stuck" the ligament to the sheath of the superficial digital flexor tendon, the tendon sheath is cut as well. Picture slicing through the heel of a too-tight sock, cutting from your Achilles tendon to just below your heel. Relieves the pressure, but not much left of the sock.

There is good reason to believe that cutting open the

annular ligament in the case of a low bow or an injured DDFT, will limit collateral damage, and pain, due to swelling and excess pressure with the annular capsule. Does this mean that clipping the annular ligament is the path toward complete rehabilitation of a racehorse or other high performance equine athlete? Again, for the same reasons as with the superior check operation, I tend to have my doubts. Let me know.

Hyaluronic Acid Injections

Hyaluronic Acid is the lubricating chemical found in synovial joints and in synovial capsules such as tendon sheaths. It has been shown that injecting a recovering tendon's sheath with hyaluronic acid speeds healing and helps prevents adhesions from forming. Other studies have suggested that HA injection into the actual torn areas of the tendon aids in healing. This is quite a promising line of investigation and a treatment I can, at least at this point in time, recommend.

PSAG

Polysulfated Aminoglycans, or PSAG, is a chemical component of connective tissue commonly used to treat cartilage disruption in joint injuries. PSAGs work by providing some of the essential structural elements in cartilage and in the bonding of collagen fibers. Adequan is one brand name of a source of I.M.-injectible PSAG. Adequan is usually given in a series of injections. Chondroitin sulfate is a food additive and can be mixed with the horse's grain. It is said to have similar effects to Adequan. There is some evidence that these chemicals will aid in the healing of bowed tendons. Very little hard information yet, though.

Antioxidant Therapy

The horse has a more hyperactive immune system than does the human. Part of the complications of healing tissues is the production of oxidative free radicals which attack healthy tissues as well as debris from damaged tissues. Free radical production can do a lot of damage immediately after a tendon injury and throughout the healing process.

There are chemicals which lock onto oxidants and render them inactive. These chemicals include: Vitamin E, Vitamin C, beta carotene (a form of vitamin A), Selenium, and Superoxide dismutase (SOD). These same nutrients will aid in recovery of minor damage to muscles and tendons after hard workouts. You should consult a performance nutritionist for dosage - I recommend Jamie Brooks at Vitaflex (802) 244-7474.

On the negative side, antioxidants inhibit tissue regeneration. If you have a genuine bow, antioxidants will help keep the area reasonably under control, with reduced inflammation, pain, and reduced tissue destruction, but when the fibers themselves are beginning to regenerate, rebuild themselves, these same chemicals will slow down that repair process. Damned if you do; damned if you don't. Best to let Mother Nature take care of healing.

BAPN

BAPN, or beta aminotropionic fumarate is a new drug that temporarily prevents cross-linking between collagen fibers in healing tendons. The drug, as of this writing, is not yet approved by the FDA, but early studies by veterinarian Ron Genovese of Cleveland (equine studies) and Dr. Bill Davis of Arizona (original human studies), indicate that it might just be the "magic bullet" that allows bowed horses to heal completely.

The whole idea behind this drug is to prevent the formation of scar tissue, collagen fibers that lay down during repair in a cross-hatched manner and not in parallel lines that will accommodate acute stresses later on. Scar tissue is formed rapidly in response to tendon injury, and that's one of the reasons we like to see the horse performing some exercise very early in the healing process - we're trying to persuade the newly forming fibers to line up in the direction of stress rather than lay down any which way.

BAPN prevents cross-linking early in the repair process, so that collagen fibers cannot form a tough protective web of scar tissue. Instead, with exercise, those fibers that aren't in line with the forces being exerted on the tendon break, while those in line survive - as long as the exercise is kept under control. Dr. Genovese uses constant ultrasound scanning to monitor the progress of healing. After about six months of BAPN treatment, the drug is stopped and serious rehabilitation begins. Another three to four months is necessary to rebuild the tendon to the point where it can approach the stress levels that injured it in the first place.

Of the last seven Thoroughbreds Dr. Genovese has completed his treatment with, all are currently racing. He has another 45 in a treatment study group that he hopes will convince the FDA that the drug is ethical for this particular problem. One horse, Onion Ring, equaled a world record after having suffered a "terrible" bow and receiving six months of the treatment regimen.

The bureaucratic FDA is expected to take at least two years to approve BAPN, even on a "breakthrough drug expedited review," and the treatment regimen will require veterinary supervision. But this is very good news for the future. Dr. Genovese practices at Thistledown in Cleveland.

Anabolic Steroids

In human medicine, anabolic steroids are often used to aid the body in rebuilding injured tissues. The breakdown of protein is called catabolism while the building of protein-based tissues is called anabolism. Anabolic steroids are somewhat misnamed because they're not really protein builders - they simply act to prevent the normal catabolism that is always going on within living cells. Instead of a protein turnover that is balanced, there is an unbalance toward tissue-building with the administration of anabolic steroids.

In horses, anabolic steroids are known as body-builders and for inducing aggressive behavior. These effects are called anabolic (constructive metabolism, or tissue-building) and androgenic (producing the effects of male hormones, hence, aggression). Some, like Equipoise, have decided androgenic effects while others, like Winstrol V, are more exclusively anabolic in effect. While no studies have been performed on equine tendon rehabilitation and anabolic steroids, it is logical that these drugs may speed recovery in the case of bowed tendons.

Electromagnetic Therapy

The whole "science" of electronic therapy began with experiments on non-healing hip fractures in elderly women. In these cases, electrodes were embedded in the bones of the patients and this caused a kind of "paste" to form, bridging the gap between the broken bone ends. With time, this paste calcified into bone. Since that time there have been many experiments with magnetic field therapy for all sorts of injuries in the horse and in humans. Most of these experiments have been inconclusive at best but there are "one rat research" anecdotes about the wonders of anything from pulsating magnetic fields to plain ice box magnets applied to various injured equine parts, including soft tissue injuries. I remain skeptical about the efficacy of all these devices.

Electrical Muscle Stimulation (EMS)

When a horse cannot bear its own weight, or the weight of a rider, safely on the injured tendon, then exercise therapy is not possible. Meanwhile, the healing process is underway, complete with inappropriate cross-hatching of collagen fiber scar tissue and adhesions forming between the tendon and its sheath. This can be an appropriate time for EMS. EMS stimulates muscles to contract. When applied to the flexor muscles of the equine leg, a kind of stationary exercise takes place that exerts some small stretching on the injured tendon.

The EMS machine is a small pack mounted on a surcingle. This pack supplies the negative charge which travels through the leads to the positive pads that are bandaged onto the targeted muscles. Of course, the intensities of these therapeutic muscular contractions must be precisely controlled. Thus the need for an experienced therapist. Again, Mimi Porter of Lexington is your best source of machines and instruction.

"Touchy-Feely" Healing

There is a large movement toward a variety of hocus-pocus healing modalities. These include certain kinds of manual manipulation and acupuncture. Do not be misled. You cannot tweak an ear, rub a nose, stick a hot tiny needle in the nostril, mind read the animal, or adjust his "energy pathways" in order to heal or help heal a bowed tendon. Medicine is medicine; religion is religion. Don't get the two confused.

Don't get me wrong. There is a place for massage therapy, and also, probably, for acupuncture. Acupuncture has not risen to the level of a science yet, although there is some research that indicates the technique can increase the flow of endorphins, the body's own morphine. There are dozens of acupuncture modalities being used by a number of acupuncturists, but most are relying on mystical Chinese literature that hasn't even a remote resemblance to science.

If you want to know how these might apply to the healing of a bowed tendon, talk to an expert physical therapist, like Mimi Porter. Not your local mind reader or wand wielder.

Chapter 12: Rehabilitating the Bowed Tendon

Bowed tendons are best rehabilitated through exercise. Designing an exercise protocol for rehabilitating a bowed tendon is impossible in general, far easier in specific. Everything depends on how severe the original injury was and what healing progress has been made as observed through ultrasound scanning. Nevertheless, I'm going to begin this chapter with a step-by-step generalized timeline, followed by expanded views of important considerations along the way. First, the timeline:

At Two Weeks:
1. If the vet approves, begin walking exercises.
2. After every exercise session, ice the tendon.
3. Continue to keep the horse quiet, maintaining reduced rations.

At One Month:
1. If ultrasound scan indicates healing is underway, gradually increase daily walking time.
2. Continue icing after exercise throughout the rehab process.
3. Check daily for any remaining signs of pain and lameness, but continue walking even when there are some signs of pain - just control the horse so that he doesn't act up and cause himself more injury.

At 90 days:
1. Ultrasound scan. Most bowed tendons will look "normal" at this point, but a scan will tell you what's actually going on in there - certainly, the tendon is far from healed.
2. If vet approves, begin weight-bearing exercise, starting with walking under saddle.

At 120 days:
1. Another ultrasound scan.
2. If everything is progressing in the right direction, increase the exercise load by moving into weight-bearing trot after a warmup of walking under saddle.

3. Be ready for setbacks - the "ladder to recovery" described below.

4. Increase the ration to support the exercise.

At 180 days:

1. Continued ultrasound scanning should show a tendon with few, if any, pockets of fluid remaining.

2. Begin slowly reconditioning the athlete for its event, starting with gradually increasing LSD at the appropriate gait.

3. Remember to ice the tendon after every workout.

4. Go to full rations.

At 260 days:

1. Begin a slow approach to event-specific exercise.

2. Ultrasound scanning will be less useful now, except for examinations when tendon acts up. If dark spots still appear in scans, continue to monitor regularly.

3. Avoid trying to protect the horse's tendon with wraps or support bandages - you want to see the first signs of oncoming trouble.

4. Use extensive warmups of walk and trot before going into higher intensity work on every "hard" day.

At 320 days:

1. A final ultrasound scan before entering into final stage of conditioning.

2. Begin full force conditioning for event, taking care to bring on increased stresses a step at a time. Keep up the overall volume of exercise.

3. Continue with icing after exercise.

4. Continue with extensive warmups (minimum 2 miles of Walk, Trot, Canter).

5. Watch the tendon for any signs of exercise intolerance.

At 360 days:

Begin competition and cross your fingers.

The timeline above may seem to be ultraconservative, and it may be, if your animal has suffered a relatively minor injury to the tendon. Still, the science says that we don't have a completely healed tendon for at least a year after injury given conventional rehabilitation, and Nature cannot be rushed. I believe, then, that the above gameplan is reasonably safe and effective. You may take more or less time if your veterinary so advises, but lean toward the cautious side of the equation.

What We're Trying To Do

An injured tendon undergoing a healing process benefits from a gradual introduction to exercise. Remember that tendons become stronger via the number of flexions or stretchings they encounter. Not only will collagen fibers be induced to organize in line to stress vectors, but strong bonds will form between them, making the tendon tougher. Adhesions will be less likely with exercise therapy, and some early adhesions can be broken before they become too strong to break with light exercise. Exercise helps collagen fibers to thicken and grow mature.

The trick is to know when and how much exercise to apply. One reason for being careful with exercise rehabilitation is the possibility of injuring the contralateral tendon - if the left fore is bowed, you just might bow the right fore with moderate exercise because the horse will be throwing extra weight onto the uninjured leg. This often happens in race horses when a bowed horse is brought back to work when the injured tendon looks good but is not actually healed. And all of this exercise should be performed on surfaces that are uniform and manicured - a track or a well-kept arena. No cross-country or uneven terrain as yet - no nasty surprises.

Now, you have to be very careful about moving on into exercise from stall rest. If the horse was an athlete before the injury, then he's going to feel a little frisky when suddenly introduced to fresh air, sunshine and a little breeze. In fact, any horse is going to be edgy coming out of confinement, and care should be taken that control of the animal is maintained at all times. If the horse starts to act up on any day during the rehabilitative exercise process, take him back to the stall - a mild tranquilizer is probably appropriate for this horse over a period of several days. Turning the horse loose in a paddock is a big mistake until all the signs of swelling and healing have subsided. Even then, a small paddock is more appropriate. Use your horse sense and prevent further injury while attempting rehabilitation.

Gradual Introduction to Exercise

Exercise rehabilitation begins with simple walking. Ten minutes a day is plenty for the first week. Here, there is no concussive stress to be absorbed, just light flexing and stretching that will tell the tendon fibers in which directions the stresses are going to be applied. Repairing fibers will align themselves appropriately. Unless the injury is so severe that a cast is required to prevent total collapse, walking should begin as soon as inflammation has been calmed to manageable levels and the animal is capable of standing on the injured leg without undue pain. In most bowed tendon cases, this is not a problem - the horse is fully capable of walking on the injured leg. After about 90 days, add a rider at the walk to slightly increase the length of the stretch of the tendon in each step. Allow at least a week for any inflammation from the extra weight of the rider to show up before moving on to the next step.

Moving on to the trot and then to the extended trot under saddle, further induces stretch and flexion while adding a concussive factor to the stresses being experienced by the tendon. With this concussion is going to come the possibility of broken adhesions occurring. Remember that a tendon must move up and down freely within its sheath. With injury, the tendon tends to adhere to its sheath or paratenon. The adhesions are likely to form during the initial stages of healing, when immobilization is one of the primary goals of the animal's healing systems. When you introduce concussive stress, these adhesions between the tendon and surrounding tissues will break - and you want them to. But there will be some swelling and heat when this occurs. While this is a necessary and painful part of the healing process, it can look like the tendon has rebowed.

The Ladder to Recovery

Don't be discouraged by what appear to be setbacks. These are normal occurrences in the rebuilding of a bowed tendon. There will be periods of clearcut improvement followed by periods of no improvement or even apparent reinjury and lameness. Unless the horse has run away with the rider or acted up in the paddock, these minor setbacks are entirely normal.

You will reach a plateau of exercise that the horse can handle, move on to another plateau and stay there for a while until the horse's body adjusts, and then move on again. It's give and take, just like everything else with horses. Two steps forward, one step back. But all of this is building stronger and stronger tendons.

When you see signs of inflammation, attack with ice and, perhaps, some anti-inflammatory medication (for short periods - three days max). Ease the exercise load for a few days. The inflamed area should calm back down and you can sneak back up and through the exercise load that broke the adhesions - only to run into some more reaction later on as the load increases. This is part of the routine of rehabilitation, not something to panic over - unless you planned to be racing back in a month.

The Devil's In The Details

Here are some details that require constant attention as you progress through rehabilitation:

1. You *must* maintain control of the horse's activities. While turning the horse out into a nice large paddock may seem "the right thing to do," unless you're completely sure the animal is not going to romp and play like a little colt, don't do it. Early turnouts should probably be introduced with a tranquilizer and later turnouts should only occur after controlled exercise has taken place.

2. Support bandages are probably not a good idea. Not only is there a chance that the bandage will be too tight and reinjure the tendon, but the whole object of rehabilitative exercise is to expose the tendon to stresses

that it must "learn" to accommodate. Again, you think you're doing something nice for your horse and you're really not.

3. I hate lungeing as exercise. It may be OK for breaking babies as long as you're using a "big circle" and are not traveling too fast with the animal, but even then, excess stresses are being conducted to the ankles and suspensories. In the case of a healing bow, lungeing opens up too many possibilities for additional injury.

4. Go light with anti-inflammatories and antioxidant vitamins during the rebuilding phase. Both suppress cell differentiation, and that is what's happening as collagen fibers are growing and aligning themselves in the rebuilding tendon. On the one hand, you want to control whatever damage may occur with inflammation, but you also want to encourage the repair and rebuilding processes. So, anti-inflammatories and antioxidants will be occasionally useful in the early stages (perhaps the first 90 days), but will become emergency-only treatments later on.

5. Remember that if you haven't corrected the original cause of the bow, be it shoeing, working surface, rider, or inappropriate exercise, you can expect a worse result this go-round.

6. Do not conclude that a "tight" tendon is a healed tendon. Even a good ultrasound result simply means that the holes in the tendon are filling in - not that the fibers are mature and strong. Take your time - it may be your last chance to save this horse's career.

7. Exercise is the best tendon rebuilder, if it is brought on gradually. All the other therapies are secondary. If you can't afford to exercise the horse, then you certainly can't afford ultrasound or laser treatments.

8. Turning out the horse is not a substitute for rehabilitative, controlled, progressively loaded forced exercise. There is some pain involved in rehabilitation and you have to grit your teeth and move your horse through it. Turning the horse out instead is just plain giving up. You'll reap what you sow.

Moving Forward

At some point, probably at about 180 days, you'll come to feel that cantering, then galloping are possible. At these gaits, care should be taken that the rider is properly balanced, the horse rounded on the bit and not pounding into the forehand. Again, you can expect some reaction to increased concussive forces. By this time, you'll have taken several ultrasound scans, and you'll be able to see clearcut progress in the healing of the tendon. If not, you're bringing on the exercise load too quickly. It's a tightrope that must be walked if your healing is to be successful and complete.

Once a comfortable lope has been established, (this Long Slow Distance should not exceed at 3:00 per mile rate) stay at that speed and build daily mileage, as if you were introducing a baby to its first forced exercise. Gradually build to a minimum of 6 continuous miles daily, tacking on a half mile of lope to the daily mileage every ten days to two weeks - and backing off whenever you get a heat/inflammation reaction.

Only when the horse is comfortable with those six miles of lope every day, only then, can you increase speed or introduce some agility/uneven terrain exercises. Do this on a single day, and then go back to loping for three or four days before going back for more of the more stressful work. This procedure will allow any minor injuries to the tendon to show themselves before additional stresses are implemented.

In subsequent chapters, we're going to take a harder look at conditioning the equine athlete. For now, you should already understand that your work is cut out for you. You know two things for sure: it can be done; there are no shortcuts.

Chapter 13: Prevention

Prevention means avoiding an injury entirely. Let's begin this chapter with the concept of prevention.

We are as gods to our horses, controlling every aspect of their daily existence. We determine how they eat, where and how they exercise, what kind of housing they occupy. We're pretty imperfect gods, too. Everything we do to and with our horses is unnatural. We reshape their lives and bodies to fit our world and our demands upon them. Some would say, myself among them, that a large dollop of responsibility comes along with playing god. Not just chores. Not just taking care of the animal, shoveling manure, providing regular exercise.

But, if we learn as much as we can about the way a horse is made and the way his body responds to the demands we make of him, then we'll become just a little better a playing god. So, let's begin at the very beginning here and see if we can't just figure out how to keep a horse from bowing tendons when we ask him to fly.

Preparing the Whole Horse

As amateur gods, we can't see inside the bodies of our athletes, and tend to rely on the impressions we get from outside the horse as to how ready he is to go on to bigger and better stresses. We're pretty good at building muscles that will hold up to the demands we make of our horses, and fairly good at building bones (I'm not counting bucked shins or splints here) that will do the same. Until something goes seriously wrong, our only clues about how we're doing in preparing the animal for an athletic contest come from the muscles of the horse. If the muscles are capable of sustaining hard exercise, then the horse won't slow down and he won't be blowing at the end of a short, hard workout. Next week, he'll do a whole lot better at the same workload, and we'll tend to move up the stress loads. If we move the load too far upscale, it's not the muscles that will go, nor, for the most part, the bones. Instead, the damn tendons will pull apart, all of a sudden, with virtually no warning - and the horse will be as surprised as we are. Somehow, we're missing the mark with tendons (and cartilage). Here's why:

As you know, tendons bridge the gaps between muscles and bones. They're harder than muscle, softer than bone. They're less stretchy than muscles, more stretchy than bone. They're more brittle than muscle, less brittle than bone. Unfortunately, they repair more slowly than either muscle or bone and, as with joint cartilage, they tend to become injured more easily than either muscle or bone. At least, that's what happens when horses do precisely what we tell them to do. And that should tell us something about what's wrong with what we're asking them to do - or how we're preparing them to do it.

Muscles and bones can be strengthened with relatively short, reasonably frequent, bouts of strenuous work. If we can bring on intensity of exercise gradually, coming finally to the full-bore athletic task, the muscles and bones will generally live through the task. But tendons and cartilage grow thicker and more resilient through repeated flexions, or bending of the joints. Cartilage thickens and becomes more dense with repetition of joint motion. Tendons get thicker and harder, developing irreducible bonds between fiber bundles and more mature collagen within those bundles, through repetition of stress. So bones and muscles depend more on the *Quality* of exercise for their strength while tendons and cartilage depend more on the *Quantity* of exercise for their strength.

On the plains in his natural environment, the horse will cover 22 miles a day on average. At a full racing gallop, the horse delivers a mile with about 200 strides. So the horse in the wild will deliver a bare minimum of 4400 flexions of the superficial digital and deep digital flexor tendons each day. Wild horses aren't being asked to race, do tricks, or carry riders over jumps. All they have to do is, once in a while, run away from predators that can't run very fast or far. Only when a wild horse is hunted relentlessly, for days, by a pack of hungry wolves, will he eventually succumb to the levels of fatigue that many "trained" horses experience in races. Even then, his tendons aren't likely to give way -

his muscles will fatigue, he'll slow down, and the wolves will catch him before he has a chance to bow a tendon.

You'll find the hardest tendons and the thickest cartilage pads on endurance racers - but none of these ever receives the number of joint flexions a wild horse experiences, except on race day, where they might just be asked to handle four times the number of flexions as the wild horse. A Quarter Horse in flat race training might experience a maximum of 200 flexions of the superficial and deep digital flexor tendons under saddle per day. They're the worst prepared of all equine athletes. Some survive the first few races, but not many. In races, their legs simply come apart at the seams.

The Key: Long Slow Distance

Get the picture? As gods, if we want to steel our horses against bowed tendons, we must deliver more overall miles. Not only that, but the miles have to come first, before the animal gets so muscle-fit that he outperforms his tendons and joint cartilage. This is why *every* equine athlete must go through a period of preliminary background mileage - Long Slow Distance. The more the better.

I tell my racehorse trainers that all their animals should gradually build to 6 continuous miles a day, every day, before any increases in speed are attempted. By "slow", I mean nothing faster than a 3:00 mile rate for gallopers, 3:30 mile rate for trotters and pacers. Even then, we have to be very careful to avoid any kind of fatigue during the rest of the training regime in order to avoid bows. And that's tricky - we're not always successful even in the most scientific of environments. It is my observation that a horse with 600 miles on him has pretty stout tendons - that's about 1 1/2 years of daily exercise in conventional Quarter Horse and Thoroughbred training circles. And these fellows are racing after 90 to 120 days of "training". That's where the researchers get all the bows to practice their various healing modalities on.

No Surprises

Prevention of bowed tendons begins with Long Slow Distance and follows along by operating under the Holiday Inn's "No Surprises" motto. But even 600 base miles is no foolproof insurance against bows. The threshold is simply raised significantly. You have to try harder to cause a tendon rupture. Still, you'll be surprised at how easily it can be done. Even the fittest horse might not survive the following all-too-common tactics.

1. If, because you are feeding properly, but not exercising the horse, the animal wants to pull, buck, run away, or otherwise misbehave, just put the pedal to the metal and let her run until she's exhausted. That'll calm her down, and heat up those tendons something fierce.

2. If the horse is misbehaving, stop feeding it, but keep on working it or racing it. The horse will settle, lose weight, get muscle sore, go anorexic, and all the tissues of its body will start weakening as the protein in them is catabolized for fuel. This technique has been proven over and over again on thousands of Thoroughbred and Quarter Horse racehorses. It'll work for you if you give it a chance. The problem here is that some other tendon or ligament, perhaps even a muscle, may rip apart before you can concentrate on the superficial or deep digital flexor tendons.

3. You get a horse shipped into the racetrack from a farm owned by an old busybody who wants to tell you your business and says that the horse has been galloping 6 miles a day, every day. Ha! You want to see right away if this horse has any potential, because the lady is going to drive you crazy and the horse had better have some earning power to put up with all that. So you slap on some racing shoes, chopping off the heels in the process, and tell the kid to go out and let her rattle for a half, just to see what she's got. This is usually good for a double bow.

4. The horse has been working great, gonna race on

Saturday, but this is Tuesday and you've gotta get in one more breeze before the race. Trouble is, it's been raining for a week and the track is deep and sloppy - the track crew isn't even touching it until just before racing starts each day. Well, the kid's gonna get dirty, but you gotta lay her down one more time before the race. Instead of her usual :47, she delivers a :52, with the kid whaling away on her down the stretch. Good for a single bow, usually the left front.

5. The horse was working hard all last week, but this week the weather's been bad and she has been cooped up in the stall for five days. Now the sun's out. Why not turn her out into the paddock? It's a little muddy, but she needs to see the light of day once in a while. Boy, look at her go! She's really feeling good! Wow! Wish I had the video camera down here. Minimum damage: tendinitis. Maximum damage: call the dead stock truck.

Four of these techniques violate Holiday Inn's principle of "No Surprises." There are hundreds of ways to violate that principle. All you have to do is show the animal a sudden increase in stresses on a particular body part. The paddock and the sloppy track exercise represent two kinds of surprises that are quite common and somewhat innocent in that the trainer actually thinks he's giving the horse what it needs. Technique 1 is somewhat rare because the trainer's peers will get after him for crippling a horse right before their eyes, obviously on purpose. But it happens. The stupidest of these is Technique 3, taking a "peek." Not only will bowed tendons result from this kind of lunacy, but bucked shins, broken bones, knee and ankle chips, muscle soreness, and perhaps even bleeding from the lungs can reasonably be expected after such an exercise.

Anyway, prevention of bowed tendons begins with Long Slow Distance and follows along by operating under the Holiday Inn's No Surprises motto. Certainly, you have to keep upgrading exercise duration and intensity, targeting in on the particular skills and athletic capabilities you're going to need in competition. You have to follow the laws of Progressive Loading and Specificity of Exercise, that is, exercise must be continuously increased on a regular basis, and that exercise must be specific to the demands of the event you're training for - a lot of trot won't help a horse gallop fast or far But everything must come a step at a time. No sudden overloadings.

And no sudden artificial changes in physique. For example, one very effective way to increase muscle size and firepower is to load the horse up with anabolic steroids. You'll get the same "pump you up" muscles that body builders and professional wrestlers proudly show off - quite suddenly. Do you know what's wrong with that approach? All of a sudden, the shoulder and hip flexor muscles can exert an extra 1,000 lb. of force on the bones they control, and that force is exerted through the tendons, which don't respond as fast to exercise and steroids as the muscles. The tendons rupture trying to transfer the much larger forces to the bones - sometimes, in human athletes, they simply pull out of the bone. In equine athletes traveling 40 mph, cascade failure: the suspensory apparatus breaks down, the bones shatter and the leg simply explodes.

Chapter 14: Fuel & Fatigue

Still, even if you follow the Long Slow Distance and No Surprises guidelines, there is no guarantee that what you've accomplished is going to be adequate to withstand the stresses that accompany the final intense stages of training and competing. Here, your biggest threat is fatigue.

With fatigue the forearm muscles, the flexor muscles that are holding up the fetlock, relax their tension, causing the tendons to absorb more of the mechanical stresses of running. The fetlocks tend to droop toward the ground, delaying breakover, and putting undue stretch on the tendons as the hoof tries to roll over the toe at the end on the stance phase of the stride. Often, the tendons experience some tearing and, once in a while, experience severe failure.

Fatigue comes in four varieties: (1) lactic acid buildup; (2) fuel depletion; (3) structural fatigue; and, (4) progressive fatigue. Any of these can bow a tendon. If you can delay fatigue so that it doesn't show up during the time your horse is training or competing, you've defeated it. You've avoided bowed tendons, at least from this cause.

Lactic Acid Fatigue: Lactic acid fatigue arises from a muscle cell paralysis due to the accumulation of lactic acid in and around fast twitch muscle cells. Lactic acid production (partially burned glycogen) occurs almost exclusively in high speed efforts. Lactic acid is produced by fast twitch muscle cells firing rapidly and hard, producing high powered output. Lactic acid appears when fast twitch muscle cells burn glycogen anaerobically, without oxygen. It's inefficient burning, that throws off waste products including lactic acid.

But for racehorses, there's still the lactic acid problem to deal with. One solution to the problem of lactic acid buildup that has recently been banned at some racetracks because it "artificially" improves performance is the "Milkshake." The vet stomach tubes the horse with a mixture of sodium bicarbonate and simple sugars just before a race. The sugars supply a boost of glycogen while the sodium bicarbonate alters the pH of the blood, buffering some of the lactic acid as it appears on the scene during the race.

A far better way to handle lactic acid is through training. Remember, the body learns to accommodate stresses if they're brought on gradually enough that no systems fail before the "conditioning" has taken hold. In the case of lactic acid, if sustained workloads that produce medium-to-high lactic acid levels are delivered, over and over again, as a part of the training protocol, then actual changes take place within the muscle cells to adjust.

What happens is that mitochondria start growing within fast twitch muscle cells. Mitochondria are the little bugs that are usually located in slow twitch muscle cells and allow the burning of fuels through the use of oxygen - the oxidative or aerobic energy pathway. Then fast twitch cells (FT) become fast twitch high oxidative cells (FTH). And when the partially burned lactic acid shows up, it can be burned the rest of the way, leaving behind carbon dioxide, water, and energy. In this way, muscle paralysis via lactic acidosis is delayed or eliminated.

Meanwhile, shorter bouts of lactate producing work will cause buffering chemicals to be formed within the bloodstream and muscle cells. So, even though lactic acid is building, it is being fought on the buffering level, as with the sodium bicarbonate blood buffering technique mentioned above. Again, fatigue is beaten back.

Fuel Depletion Fatigue: It is unlikely that an endurance racer will ever suffer from lactic acid fatigue. Endurance horses seldom compete at full speed, or even half speed. Their fatigue problem centers around muscle fuel depletion and the resulting wobbliness of ketosis (accelerated burning of fatty acids by the liver, as during starvation) due to the burning of alternate fuels like fat and protein. Fuel depletion of slow twitch muscle cells, which endurance athletes preferentially recruit, is quite difficult. These cells can burn the alternative fuels, and there never is a huge demand being made. To gradually deplete all the fuels available to slow twitch muscle cells requires hours and hours of steady exercise. Fit human cyclists working at 70% maximum output require 4 hours of continuous exercise before exhausted slow twitch cells are forced to pass the workload on to the easily fatigued fast twitch cells in their bodies.

Fast-moving horses, however, can quickly run into a fuel depletion problem. That's because the working muscle cells, the fast twitch, can only burn glycogen. Glycogen is stored within the muscle cells, is present in the blood stream, and is used as an exclusive fuel for the brain. When glycogen stores drop precipitously, mechanisms within the body begin to inhibit glycogen burning in the fast twitch muscles in order to preserve some brain fuel. So fast twitch muscle cells can still contain 25-30% of their glycogen stores and yet be slowed down or shut down. Of course, if the horse goes into competition fuel deficient, as many racehorses do, then fuel fatigue comes on even faster.

Prevention of fatigue and subsequent tendon injury can be accomplished by eliminating the cause. In the case of fuel depletion, all that is necessary is to ensure that the muscle cells are stacked to the gills with fuel. One way to ensure adequate fuel supplies is to never allow the horse to lose weight. You want him gaining weight from the onset of training, when the horse is "fat", until the day of performance. If you deliver proper exercise, there will be no excess fat on the horse, and the added weight will be expanded muscle capacity and muscle fuel.

Feed the horse so he can work. A simple concept, but seldom utilized - at least at the racetrack. Instead, the trainer cuts the horse's rations because he misbehaves, but doesn't reduce the workload. The horse slowly starves as it continues to work, albeit slower and slower. You see, we have all these experts out there who know nothing about exercise and the physiological results of exercise who will take one look at a well-muscled horse and proclaim, "Too fat, too fat!" They'll tell you the horse needs to lose 150 lb. before it can safely perform. If you believe them, you'll begin starving your horse while you go blissfully on training a suddenly placid horse. As the weight comes off, you'll notice a reduced enthusiasm for work, and occasional sorenesses or stiffnesses from unknown sources.

In time, the animal will start burning body tissues for fuel, protein. You might start smelling a metallic breath from him - ketosis. What you don't see is that throughout his body, protein is being catabolized, broken down and transported to where it's needed - the working muscles. All the tissues of his body are getting weaker and weaker. Then you go to competition, even though you're not real happy with the animal's attitude or abilities. You lose, but worse, the horse bows a tendon. Or pulls a muscle. Or blows a suspensory. Or twists a gut. Anything can happen.

The truth about "fatness" in performance horses is this: if you're working the horse daily, and twice a week are really drilling him for his event, then you can feed him all he can eat, every day, up to or more than 25 pounds of grain a day, and his body weight will level off at that weight which is appropriate for his best performance in his event - so will his appetite. And the increased body weight is going to be all muscle, or should I say stored muscle fuel and enzymes. If you take your time and deliver lots of the right kind of work for your horse's event, his body will reshape itself precisely to accommodate the target activity. And you won't have to worry about tendons melting away.

The fuel we're talking about comes from grains. Sweet feed, corn, oats, etc. A good sweet feed mix, like Carnation Superhorse, TizWiz, Omolene 300, or a local mill's mix that is approximately 50% corn and 50% oats is the best source of carbohydrate. If your horse performs in events lasting longer than 3 minutes, then a fat-containing feed, like Purina's Athlete, may be a good solution. Forget hay and grass as suitable sources of carbohydrate. Not enough firepower there for a hard-working equine athlete.

In addition to normal carbohydrate feeding, you can "top off the tank" with glycogen loading. This is a technique that once consisted of several days of forced muscle fuel depletion - semi-starvation while going ahead with workouts. Then came four to five days of reduced workloads and consuming 1/3 more carbohydrates than were in the normal daily diet. Physiologists said that this provided a 25% boost in stored muscle glycogen. Coaches and athletes said that glycogen loading improved their performance times by 2 seconds in a 2-minute event.

We've had the same experience with horses, but have avoided the depletion stages because horses get cranky and sore when their feed intake is cut and they're asked to continue working. The latest science from the human researchers tells us that the depletion stage is really not necessary anyway - a 1/3 increase in carbohydrate (sweet feed or straight cracked corn) intake four days out from an event gives a 25% increase in stored glycogen all by itself.

Then there's fat in the form of corn oil added to the feed. It has long been known that high fat diets are good for endurance athletes because slow twitch muscle cells can burn fat as a fuel using oxygen. And fat is a longer lasting, more efficient fuel than glycogen/carbohydrates. Great for endurance athletes, but not so hot for events involving speed and fast twitch muscle cells.

But then came a study from Louisiana State concerning the feeding of 1/3 of a cup of corn oil over each grain ration. The corn oil enabled racing Thoroughbreds to avoid fatigue to the same extent that those on glycogen loading diets do - but for a different reason. In this case, corn oil feeding had the effect of eliminating ketones from the blood. Remember, ketones are the product of protein burning, and act as a warning system to the rest of the body that glycogen stores are low and protein is being catabolized. The higher the ketone level, the less muscle glycogen depletion is permitted. With no ketones in the blood, muscle cells were allowed to burn nearly all their glycogen. Thus, they reach the point of fatigue later in the event.

Structural Fatigue and Progressive Fatigue: Structural fatigue is best illustrated by the bending of a paper clip until it breaks. Less dangerous, but still a threat to tendons in the long run is progressive fatigue or chronic metabolic fatigue. In this case, the fueling and enzyme systems don't have time to recover and rebound between hard workouts. The results, and signs, of progressive fatigue are similar to those you experience when you're not providing enough nutrition to support the workload. In general, you can consider structural fatigue as a result of too much speed too soon, while chronic metabolic fatigue is more a result of too quick an increase in overall energy expenditure. Still, tendons can suffer from going too long too soon, even at slow rates of speed. Especially if the toes are too long and the heels too low and underslung.

Work/Rest/Recovery/Rebound

As you've probably already guessed, the trick is to get in enough lactate-producing work, while avoiding the fatigue that lactic acid causes, during training. Later, we'll talk about recovery heartrates and what they mean in terms of lactic acid buildup and fatigue. Now let's talk about the kind of work necessary to strengthen the animal's resistance to lactic acid fatigue, structural and progressive fatigue. The basis of this work is paying attention to the conditioning cycle. The conditioning cycle becomes more important as you increase the intensity of exercise, but sometimes even building background mileage requires periods of rest and recovery.

Achieving a conditioning effect is a matter of showing the athlete a stressful workload. Then a brief period of "rest" allows the athlete to repair any damage done during the workout - and damage is done to most of the involved organs if the workout is going to produce a conditioning effect, or adaptation. Now, no athlete undergoing a sophisticated training regime needs a day off. Remember, some 90% of the blood vessels of the body are shut down when the athlete is simply standing still - The "rest" days are simply days of reduced workload containing no intense exercise. Some work is necessary in the days after a hard workout in order to flush away debris from damaged tissues and bring in repair troops and nutrients. .

So a hard workout should be followed by two or three days of "rest" exercise. For example, I might have built a Thoroughbred to gallop six continuous miles daily. And then I'll have introduced him to interval training days that begin with a warmup followed by three increasingly faster miles separated by ten minute rest periods. The interval workouts expose the horse to gradually higher lactic acid levels, but they're stressful, and the horse will need recovery days after such a workout. The day-after recovery work for a horse as described above: three miles easy lope. The day after that, four miles easy lope. Then, depending on the horse and his recovery cycle, another four easy miles or another interval workout.

During the rest days, muscle fuel and enzymes are replenished. Repairs are made to all systems that were abused in the hard workout. When full recovery is achieved, sometimes within 24 hours, but more often over 48 hours, the body goes further, with rebound. Another word for rebound is supercompensation. It means that the body prepares itself to perform work beyond what was asked for in the last hard workout, in order that it doesn't sustain damage this time. What the body doesn't know is that we're going to keep on asking for a little bit more with each workout: progressive loading. Thus, every workout we perform will cause further adaptation, step by step, until we have the athletic ability we're looking for - that's what conditioning is all about.

However, if our workouts come on too quickly, that is, if the stresses - speed in this case - are elevated too quickly from workout to workout, then more damage will be done than can be repaired and supercompensated within 2 or 3 days. As far as the tendons are concerned, we'll slowly drive them into structural fatigue. There is also the risk of progressive or chronic metabolic fatigue if you fail to give the horse enough recovery time or enough nutritional support.

Both of these fatigues can be avoided with good horsemanship and/or scientific monitoring. On the horsemanship side, a fully recovered horse is going to be begging for work. He'll have regained whatever weight was lost during the last workout. He'll show no signs of stiffness - including the day after the workout. Of course there will be no clinical signs of damage, such as filling, wind puffs, heat, etc. And no psychological signs: head down, turned to the back of the stall, lying down, off feed, crankiness, refusal to work, etc. I don't know what causes this, but there will be no dark shiny ring around the eyes, either, except with some Arabs.

Scientifically, both structural and progressive fatigue can be spotted through monitoring. Morning resting heartrates, and working heartrates, will be slightly higher until the horse has fully recovered. Body temperature may be slightly elevated as recovery is taking place. Muscle enzymes, like SGOT, CPK, and LDH will be more active in the blood until recovery is complete. With longterm chronic metabolic (or progressive) fatigue, the monocyte count will rise above 5%. If your horsemanship clues suggest something's not quite right, take blood tests for muscle enzymes and monocytes. If you find nothing there, then start worrying about structural damage somewhere in the body.

You can help your horse make it through the initial stages of the recovery process by feeding antioxidants: Vitamin E, Selenium, Vitamin C, beta carotene, and other, more exotic, chemicals like Superoxide Dismutase (SOD) and some branched chain amino acids. Here's the story as I wrote it for my newsletter, *Racing Science Review* in February, 1993:

Oxidant Stress

Vitamin E. Vitamin C. Selenium. What's the magic here? Why, all of a sudden, are we hearing about these nutrients from every direction when, just a few years ago, scientists and nutritionists were saying that claims of the miracles supposedly wrought by them were unproven? Because science is now catching up to practical experience. These chemicals, as well as beta carotene (a form of Vitamin A), Super Oxide Dismutase (SOD), Cystine (an amino acid), and other, less understood chemicals, like DMG, MSM, and Coenzyme Q10, are now known to be antioxidants. To understand how they work, and how chemicals like Iron, Ozone, and polyunsaturated fats can do a great deal of damage, you have to understand the concept of Oxidant Stress. Let's have at it, shall we?

Exercise scientists have traditionally thought of oxygen as "can't get too much of a good thing". We measure the success of conditioning by way of oxygen uptake and oxidative capacity. But oxygen availability is a two-edged sword. Every major disease and pathological process involves oxygen radicals destroying living tissue. Think of it this way: if you're going to build a fire using oxygen, then the surrounding materials better be fireproof. That's where the antioxidants come in. They protect cells from the highly oxidative free radicals that pop up with hard exercise, disease, and trauma.

First, let me give you the scientific definition of a free radical: a molecule or molecular fragment containing an unpaired electron in the valence shell. There are lots of kinds of free radicals, but the ones we're concerned about in this discussion are those that result from oxidative chemistry. Oxidation occurs by adding oxygen, removing hydrogen, or transferring electrons. Transferring electrons is what occurs inside mitochondria, those little bugs we want to populate fast twitch muscle cells with. And transferring electrons as a mode of oxidation is where free radicals are produced. About 5% of the oxygen used in mitochondrial energy production ends up as part of free radicals called superoxides.

Are you with me so far? Well, it gets a hell of a lot more complicated, but let's suffice to say here that superoxide free radicals attack cell structures, eating them for breakfast and wreaking havoc. On the other side of the war are free radical scavengers, which eat superoxides for breakfast. Superoxide Dismutase is one of these; another is glutathione peroxidase. Both of these normally appear in cell makeups - the more conditioning the cells has had, the more SOD and GPX are stored away in cell membranes as protection.

There are other molecules that are free radical scavengers because they react with free radicals. Among these are Ascorbate (forms of vitamin C) , Vitamin E, Vitamin A (especially as beta carotene), unsaturated fatty acids, unsaturated amino acids, and sugars. When heavy work, disease, or trauma take place, free radicals are produced that tend to overwhelm cell defenses like SOD and GPX. Excess iron or copper in the diet aids the enemy - producing extremely reactive free radicals.

There's another common feed additive that can cause oxidant stress: corn oil. Yep, our additive for increased fuel use in fast twitch muscle cells, according to the Louisiana

State paper cited in a recent issue. If you leave corn oil in sunlight, or hot weather, it degrades, turning into almost all free radicals. You'll get the glycogen-sparing, ketone-reduction effect, but you'll also reap increased tissue destruction. That is, unless you're supplementing with free-radical scavengers.

Worse is supplementing iron, as in Red Cell and the other mixes that are loaded with iron. In talking to Jamie Brooks at Vitaflex, I found that the company is reducing the percentages of iron in their mixes. It turns out that iron is probably the most prooxidant chemical out there - it's called a "transition metal". Copper is another.

The papers I'm reading can be found in <u>Medicine and Science in Sports and Exercise</u> Volume 25, number 2, February, 1993 in a Symposium: Oxidant Stress, Aging, and Exercise. Free radicals, according to this group of studies, can be blamed for aging, inflammation, cancer, synovial fluid degradation, and cell destruction - especially muscle cells in athletes. Thus, the old miracle claims for antioxidants, like Vitamins C & E, seem to hold more water.

Of course, these are studies, two of them looking at how exercise, then Vitamin E, protect athletes from post-exercise cell damage. One study measured levels of malondialdehyde, a "hyperoxide" produced in strenuously exercising muscles. Trained athletes produced 1/3 less free radicals after exercise than did untrained subjects. Within 30 minutes post exercise, trained subjects had eliminated all free radicals while the untrained maintained half the post exercise levels. In another study, free radical production post exercise was cut by 2/3 with Vitamin E supplementation.

Vets go to great lengths to fight inflammation because they realize that severe swelling will cause a lot of additional tissue destruction. Oxidative stress, in the form of free radicals, plays a major part in this tissue destruction. Intense exercise itself throws off free radicals in huge numbers. This explains why some trainers who've been feeding higher than normal doses of E and Selenium have said that their horses recovery more quickly from races and workouts, showing less stiffness and soreness. It may also be the reason that recovery from tying up is quicker with E and Se *supplementation.*

The Vitamin E study was conducted with humans on a daily dose of E at 200 milligrams. Normally, vitamin E is measured in International Units. Other papers used daily doses of 400 to 1200 IU and got similar results. Some of the studies showed an ergogenic performance enhancement from E supplementation. Here's a part of the conclusions of the 200 page paper:

"Oxidative stress associated with exercise seems to be better tolerated by trained subjects working at moderate intensity and not to exhaustion. This has been indicated by lower levels of lipid peroxidation by-products in trained compared with untrained subjects. But trained persons are not totally protected from oxidative stress. Several studies have reported both trained and untrained persons suffered inflammation and muscle damage from exercise-induced lipid peroxidation reactions in synovial fluid in the knee joint, creatine kinase in plasma and muscle, and an increased DNA damage-and-repair cycle activity as measured in urine. The type and intensity of exercise are important considerations since they will ultimately determine the mechanism of free radical reactions.

"This is not real good news for racehorses, because it is high intensity exercise that sends the free radical count out the roof. The lesson for us: back off the iron supplements and bring on E, C, Se, SOD, and beta carotene. Fireproof those muscle cells! And keep up the conditioning.

On the other hand, oxidant chemicals promote cell differentiation, and that's what's happening when a bowed tendon is healing and all that granulation tissue is present. Using antioxidants then will slow down healing. It's always something, isn't it?

Chapter 15: Heartrate Monitoring and Interval Training

In another book in this series, we'll be taking a hard look at monitoring the heartrate of exercising horses in order to achieve an appropriate level of fitness without crossing the line of fatigue and subsequent injury. Your horse's working heartrate, taken by using an onboard heartrate monitor, can tell you exactly how hard the animal is working, and how close to fatigue he's getting during a work session. It works much like a tachometer on a racecar - engine RPMs. I'll briefly explain working heartrate and recovery heartrate, and how you can use the recovery heartrate numbers to condition your horse while stopping short of damaging fatigue.

The highest normal heartrates every recorded in a racing horse hover around 240. Most horses in a race seldom exceed 224 beats per minute. The lowest resting heartrate ever recorded is 19 BPM in a champion endurance racer. Normal resting heartrate in a reasonably fit horse standing quietly in a stall ranges from 33 to 40 beats per minute.

As soon as the saddle goes on, anticipation of coming events will rev the heartrate up to 80 BPM, and, with the rider up and the horse walking toward the working environment, excitement will push the heartrate further - perhaps to 110. Some horses are quite nervous in the working environment and they'll show their nervousness with even higher heartrates at a walk. This increase is called an emotional "artifact."

Once the exercise is well underway, the heartrate will settle into a "working" heartrate that has little or no emotional artifact present. A fit loping horse will probably tick over at somewhere between 140 and 160 beats per minute - with the emotional horse sometimes retaining a 30-beat artifact, pushing its heartrate up to as high as 190 for the same light work. Maintaining this kind of heartrate is hard work all by itself, and such a horse will fatigue sooner, but not as quickly as when the 190 is a genuine "working" heartrate.

And 190 is about where a fit horse starts producing lactic acid in quantity. While racehorses can sustain workloads that push the heartrate above 215 for two minutes or more, crossing the 190 threshold is the first milestone in oncoming fatigue. Your horse, depending on its level of fitness, may not be able to sustain 190 for a full two minutes. But some horses can go "all day" at 190.

Immediately after exercise, the heartrate begins dropping, then remains static for a short period before it drops again to a resting rate. This static period, or plateau, occurs between 60 and 90 seconds after cessation of exercise and is called the recovery heartrate. Recovery heartrate is the most important number you can obtain from your horse. It's the recovery heartrate that tells you just how much lactic acid was built up during a workout, or a portion of a workout. If a lot of lactate has been produced, the body informs the heart that an "oxygen debt" have been incurred, and the heart maintains a higher rate, even when the horse is standing still. If no lactic acid was produced during a workout, then, immediately after shutdown of the work, the heartrate will plummet, crossing the 100 mark in its downward spiral within 90 seconds of stopping the exercise.

Somewhere along that downward spiral, comes the plateau, where the heartrate flattens out and either doesn't drop, or drops very slowly. A horse could have hit 200 BPM during a work, and the heartrate will drop to 170 within five seconds of coming to a walk. In another five seconds, 150, at 30 seconds after the work has stopped: 130 and still dropping, 125, 120, 116, 110, 104, 99, 98, 99, 100 - that's your plateau. Another horse might have built some lactic acid during the work at 200 BPM, and his recovery spiral might go: 200, 180, 170, 155, 145, 140, 135, 130, 125, 120, 118, 117, 117, 118 - and again, you've reached your plateau, as sometime between 60 and 90 seconds after the workout has stopped. In the last example, we'd call 117 the "recovery heartrate."

A recovery heartrate in excess of 105 indicates that some lactic acid was created during the exercise. At a recovery of 110, you're getting in some good conditioning that will help prevent fatigue in competition or in later workouts. A recovery heartrate above 120 tells you that you're building a considerable lactate level, and fatigue is just around the corner. At a 130 recovery, the horse has had enough for today. In excess of 135, shut the workout down now and pray you haven't hurt the horse.

You don't need an expensive heartrate monitor to get the recovery heartrate. All you have to do is get off the horse and use a stethoscope or simply your hand on the left side of the chest near the elbow. Count the heartbeats for ten seconds, then multiply by six to get Beats Per Minute. Keep doing that every few seconds until your horse has plateaued. That is, until you get the same heartrate, or one within a beat or two, for several counts in a row. That's your recovery heartrate, as far as lactic acid, fatigue, and bowed tendons is concerned.

If you break up your workouts into sections, and you monitor heartrate recoveries, then you'll always have a very good idea about the level of fatigue your horse is experiencing, and you can always shut down the workout before fatigue takes over and a bow, or another kind of a misstep, occurs. Interval training is one kind of exercise design that allows this safety procedure to come into full use. What is interval training?

Interval Training

Interval training is breaking a workout into several bouts of relatively intense exercises, with partial-recovery rest periods (intervals) between. For example, a racehorses training to race a mile might perform a workout consisting of a nice warmup of about 2 1/2 miles of Walk Trot Canter (WTC), then roll into the first of four 3/4 mile bursts, the first slow, that last at near racing rates. Between each heat is a rest period of WTC that lasts exactly seven minutes.

The heartrate of the horse is monitored onboard throughout the workout, and when recovery heartrates begin to exceed 125, the workout is either shut down, or the distance or the speed of the next heat is curtailed. If you follow the rules of interval training, it's extremely hard to bow a horse through fatigue - but at the same time, you're building an animal that can withstand extended bouts of high speed because he's developing mitochondria within his muscle cells in order to deal with lactic acid when it appears.

In all of these heats of exercise, the working heartrate is going to exceed 190 in a fit horse. That's because his lactic acid threshold, the heartrate at which lactic acid really starts to build up, gets higher and higher as the animal becomes fitter. In the beginning of training, a 140 to 160 running heartrate may trigger some significant lactic acid production, so you have to sneak up on higher heartrates for extended distances (more than a half mile). Four months into a good, progressively loaded conditioning program, though, the threshold might be up around 190. In a lot of articles I've read lately, there is erroneous advice to avoid heartrates over 160, or to avoid them over 200 later on. If you follow that advice, your horse will never be prepared to deliver significant speed over a route of ground. If you try it without having prepared him for sustained speed, the animal will bow, or come up with another fatigue-related injury.

As always, the recovery heartrate will tell you if you're getting the right level of exercise accomplished, or if you're going too slow to get anything useful done. Here's how: You've just done a piece of work - let's say you galloped a mile at a strong lope (a lope is a collected gallop, faster than a canter but still rounded on the bit). As you pull up, the countdown begins for that 60-90 second space where the heartrate is going to plateau as it drops. You come to a canter, to a trot, and then to a walk. You might even stand for a while, and let the horse look back over the course he's traveled. Somewhere in this walking or standing mode, the plateau is going to occur, and it'll happen within 90 seconds of your beginning to pull the horse up.

If the recovery is below 100, you really didn't do any lactic acid tolerance work - even if you've just done a lot of mileage and the horse is tired. In that case, your horse is becoming fatigued for lack of muscle fuel, or possibly from a high body temperature. If the respiration rate stays high while the heartrate quickly drops below 100, you're experiencing heat stress in your horse - he's trying to blow off heat with his "panting". Better shut the workout down and start earlier tomorrow. A recovery heartrate under 110 is OK, and shows that some lactic acid was experienced during the workout, but not really enough for the animal to get a strong conditioning effect. Recovery heartrates from 110 to 120 indicate good conditioning workouts.

A Sample Interval Training Program

In preparing a Thoroughbred racehorse to deliver a competitive performance at a mile or longer, I begin by building the animal to six continuous miles at an open lope (somewhere around a 3:00 rate). This can take four months or more in a baby, or as little as 45 days with a horse coming back off a turnout - a horse that has done such workloads before. Once that workload is accomplished and the horse has delivered it for a week without showing any signs of difficulty, I'll move into slow intervals, as follows:

First, I cut the daily "off" day mileage to four continuous miles of open lope, warming up with about a mile of walk and trot before starting the lope. Once every three or four days is a "work" day. Before the workout, the horse will warm up with a half-mile trot and a mile of easy lope. I don't do a lot of cantering with a racehorse because cantering is not a racing stride, and I want the horse performing with exactly the same muscles operating in exactly the same coordination mode for most of the conditioning miles. In the workout, the horse will deliver three one-mile heats with ten minute active rests between. An active rest is Walk, Trot, Canter, Walk - ad lib. A horse that can lay down six 3:00 miles can easily deliver a 3:00, 2:50, and 2:40 mile, and this is where I'll start the intervals.

That 3 X 1 mile workout will gradually get faster and faster. In a month (about eight workouts later) the horse should be able to deliver his triples in 2:30, 2:20, 2:10. I'll take him down to 2:20, 2:10, 2:00 or faster before moving into a different mode: 4 X 3/4 mile workouts with seven minute active rests between. If I have a horse delivering that last 3 X 1 workout, with a 2:00 mile at the end, then it should be easy for him to do a 4 X 3/4 workout in 1:40, 1:37, 1:33, 1:30. That workout would then progress, week by week, until the horse is delivering 1:24, 1:21, 1:18, 1:14.

Now, you'd think a horse that has done all that work would be pretty fit for racing. Well, the horse is very fit, but not yet for racing. If I raced him as he is, he'd go out fast, hit a brick wall, fade away, and then come back to the saddling paddock ready for more work, hardly blowing at all.　What's missing is the chemistry for speed that I'm going to be talking about next.　No problem; it's just a matter of a brief tapering out.

Maintaining the 4-mile "off" days, I'll shift to a series of double 5/8ths, easy/hard, on the same 3-4 day "workout" schedule as before. I'll start with a pair of 5/8ths in 1:10, 1:05 with full recovery between. These are speed-specific sprint workouts - for a miler racehorse. Next, a 1:10, 1:03 workout. Then a 1:10, 1:01. Then a 1:10, 1:00. When I crack a minute for that second 5/8ths, I've got a racehorse that is chemically and physically safe to compete at anywhere from 3/4 of a mile to 1 1/2 miles. If, for some reason, I don't get all the speed I'm looking for, I can always move on to double halves with open (full recovery) rest periods. If I hang around in speed-specific territory too long, though, I'll start losing some of the endurance or stamina I've built with the interval workouts.

In any case, this horse is very unlikely to bow, or to experience any other major injury, in a race or a workout. Interval training programs can be designed for all types of performance horses, including endurance horses, eventers, hunters, and even show horses. Interval training in the early stages will also make things easier for sprinting types:

Short Stuff

There is a reason Carl Lewis works six hours a day, 364 days a year, to prepare himself of a 10-second Olympic sprint. You should keep Carl in mind as you train your sprinting horse. If anything, sprinters need more protective conditioning than distance animals, and your regimen should start with Long Slow Distance, just as in the longer going animals.

Cardiovascular development is just as important in sprinters as in the longer runners, but for a different reason. It's not oxidative capacity that you're looking for here, but a set of lungs that won't explode under the extreme internal pressures sprinters develop in 22 seconds of all-out effort. While some 65% of race runners bleed from the lungs during a race, when a sprinter bleeds, it's an explosion. They die right before your eyes.

The same Long Slow Distance training that protects the cardiovascular system also protects the tendons and ligaments. Speed is easy to come by, because a lot of it is developed chemically within the muscles and the nerves serving them. It's very easy, then, to get the muscles all fired up so that the horse can really gobble up some ground. Three or four speed workouts, one every three or four days, will really bring on the horse's natural speed capabilities. But speed can be dangerous because of the high levels of stretch and concussion it produces. Those workouts will leave the structural components, tendons, bones and cartilage, behind in development because the changes needed are tissue changes, not chemical changes. So, you can easily train a horse to outrun his legs with sprint workouts that are brought on too soon or too quickly. The reward is a fat, juicy bow.

You should always approach speed very gradually, from longer and slower works to shorter and faster, over a period of months. This will allow you to deliver a larger volume of overall work in order to build stronger tendons, step by step. Again, my rule of thumb is that, if your horse can't deliver six continuous miles of open lope, he has no business going faster than a 2:20 mile rate. No business galloping a quarter mile in faster than 35 seconds. And it takes months to build a horse to six continuous miles of lope (about a 3:00 rate per mile or 40 second quarter) if he's never done that before - no matter what kind of winning performance he accomplished last year.

By the way, if you want to train in firepower, but you want to avoid knee-crushing concussion in doing so, find a hill and do "resistance" workouts. The heats will be slower, but the conditioning effect is speed.

If you're training a sprinter, as for barrel racing or flat racing a quarter mile, lactic acid won't play much of a part in the overall scheme of things unless, as a part of your training regime, you work through a period of extended, strong gallops (this is something I would recommend, because sustained high heartrate work also develops a stronger heart and lungs). Short sprints, though, won't cause lactic acid to build unless the rest periods between multiple short sprints are too short (as short as the sprint itself). Generally, when you train specifically for speed, you give full recovery between heats, that is, the heartrate drops below 100 before you turn and roll out the next sprint. With interval training, your horse's heartrate may still be hovering around 110 or higher when your roll into the next heat.

In the final stages of training a sprinter, the workouts will be fast, but the process won't be interval training. Instead, it's "repetitions", with full recovery between heats. Reps allow the athlete to get in enough volume at high speeds in order to achieve a conditioning effect. The problems you encounter here are two: high speed fuel depletion and high core body temperatures. The "safety valve" for the first: when the horse starts to slow down, from one heat to the next, stop the workout, call it a day. Recognizing heat stress is easy: the horse will start dancing and prancing, flashing his tail, misbehaving. His heartrate will recovery normally, but his respiration rate will remain elevated.

Reading one chapter does not make an exercise physiologist. But now, you should have some idea of how science can help you: 1) condition your horse; and, 2) prevent injuries. It's proven, established stuff, and it's out there. Use it.

Chapter 16: Teaching Stupid Legs

Ever have somebody come up behind you and tap you behind the knees? Your legs collapse because the golgi tendon organs in the tendons at the rear of the knee complain instantly and vehemently to the central nervous system that they're being overstretched. And the central nervous system, without the brain's knowledge or permission, instantly shuts down all the muscle firings that are holding you upright. The same thing happens when you step on a rock the wrong way and, instead of wrenching your ankle, the whole leg collapses. It's a sign of neuromuscular intelligence.

Part of the conditioning effect of any kind of exercise is "motor learning," or the development of neuromuscular coordination. All motion in the equine athlete is a delicate balance of millions of signals jumping back and forth from the nervous system, muscle cells, and sensory organs. the sum of all this messaging activity is called neuromuscular coordination. In everyday language, it's called skill. Whatever the name, it is something that must be learned, just as driving a car or riding a bicycle must be learned. Equine athletes begin their careers with stupid legs that must be taught to safely perform movements that aren't natural. There are lots of problems to overcome, and the first of these is the battle between agonist muscles and their antagonists - on the other side of the joint. For example, the foreleg of the horse has flexor muscles connected to bone via the flexor tendons - but, in the front of the legs are extensor muscles connected via extensor tendons - these tendons can become injured, too, but we don't call them bows when they do. Flexors bend the joint; extensors straighten the joint.

The horse's agonists are continually fighting the antagonists for permission to go ahead and do the work the human is asking them to do. For example, going faster means that millions more muscle cells must fire simultaneously, exerting far more tension through tendon to bone. The antagonists resist this effort just to keep the leg from flying off should the agonists become too enthusiastic. Before this catastrophe can happen, though, the tendons on both sides of the joint start to squeal for help from the central nervous system. The CNS will shut down its commands to the agonists and the horse will have to go slower.

To an extent, we humans can override at least a part of this protective mechanism by vehemently asking the animal for more speed. When we do, bowed tendons and other injuries are a likely result. If, instead, we bring on the speed gradually enough for the involved body parts to strengthen, and for the agonists and antagonists to come to an agreement that the extra forces involved can be safely accommodated, then we'll finally get our extra speed in a safe manner.

But that's only half the problem. Remember my analogy of the hoof as a ball on the end of a chain? The hoof is controlled by muscles that are quite remote from it. In order to avoid injury, that hoof has to fly through the air, loosely wobbling as it goes, and then touch down in precisely the right way. If it doesn't land properly, huge unexpected forces shoot up the leg to impact bone, cartilage, tendons, ligaments and muscles.

Go For Wand's tragic death in the Breeder's Cup is an example of hoof flight going wrong, in this case because of fatigue. The foreleg is supposed to curl forward, snap into a straight, locked position, and then begin traveling rearward, before the hoof hits the ground. A fatigued horse at the gallop shortens its stride, and if that shortening goes to far, the leg barely has time to snap into its straight position before the hoof impact. There is no rearward motion, to substantially reduce the forces of impact. Go For Wand's foreleg snapped in one of these fatigue-induced pogo stick hoof impacts.

Even when fatigue is not a factor, the uneducated foreleg can make mistakes in hoof placement. Remember that every increment of new speed, every change in running surface, every change in the position or weight of the rider, every change in shoeing, every change in the weight of the horse, every change in directional patterns, every exposure to a new kind of terrain - each of these requires a sometimes substantial change in neuromuscular coordination. And the body can make mistakes, will make mistakes, as it adjusts. Big demands for adjustment mean big mistakes. And big mistakes mean bowed tendons and other injuries. We call them missteps, a rather dainty word considering the damage that is being done. Go For Wand took a misstep; so did Ruffian, and so do tens of thousands of hurried-along equine athletes each year.

Since we have taken on the responsibility of being our horses' gods, we must be aware of all the little nuances of biomechanics we ask our horses to face. We have to make sure the legs get educated, a step at a time, to the new demands we're introducing. Here's how it works:

When a new task is asked of the horse, primitive messages are sent to the muscles, almost on a spray and pray basis. The movement is necessarily clumsy. Meanwhile, screeches and hollers from the affected parts come sailing back along the lines of communication - afferent nerves, to be exact - telling the controlling parts of the central nervous system that it's insane asking for such moves - some parts saying, "That's it! I quit!" But we gods repeat the request, time after time, and gradually the central nervous system gets all its ducks in a row, beefing up the command routes for the new movement by sending neurotransmitting chemicals down to those neurons that are in direct control of exactly the right muscle groups needed to accomplish the task. This chemical spinup takes about five days - you'll see the results of today's practice sometime next week.

Eventually then, after many repetitions of the same task or skill, all parties involved become educated to perform their roles in the production of the new movement. At some point in this process, the horse's conscious mind stops controlling the movement. The mind is way too slow to control quick, near-reflex motions. Imagine if you had to think about what to do with your hands as you were driving down a superhighway. Reflexes have to be automatic and all fast and precise motor functions must be trained-in, not thought about each time an athlete wants to run.

Instead of slow brainwork, a little "computer program", called an engram, takes over the job of handling all the commands involved in executing a human order to, say, "turn left on a dime". Suddenly, you have smart legs - at least for that movement, at that speed, over that terrain, on those shoes, with that rider balanced in that way, etc., etc., etc. Let me give you an example:

During the first five years of my foray into horse racing, I trained Trotters and Pacers to race. Now, asking a horse to trot a mile faster than two minutes is like asking yourself to crawl on your hands and knees for a half mile nearly as fast as you can run it. The horse's natural gaiting system commands the horse to move from a trot to a canter or gallop at a certain speed. When we train a trotter or pacer to race, we're asking the horse's body to violate that system, in a very big way: the normal trot delivers a 5:00 mile, while a very extended trot may crack 4:00. We're asking horses to maintain the trot at speeds more than twice that fast.

Sometimes the learning is surprisingly sudden and dramatic, as when a pacer learns to roll from side to side so that his hooves can hit the ground at the midline of his body - that's far more efficient, allowing for more speed at less cost. And it happens overnight sometimes. You'll be training 2:10 miles, time after time, and the horse seems hopelessly deadlocked at that speed, stiff-legged, working as hard as he can but making no progress from workout to workout. Then one day his butt starts to wag back and forth before your eyes and, when the training mile is finished, you look at your watch and see a nice 2:05. I call it a breakthrough workout.

Similar things happen to trotters on the way to 2:00 miles, but they are lesser adjustments and happen all the way along the training curve - the trot is a more complicated gait and neuromuscular intelligence must be achieved in small increments. Push the trotter and all sorts of problems crop up, including bowed tendons. This is because the trot is a more complex gait and the animal requires time to develop the neuromuscular coordination necessary to take the gait to a very unnatural 2:00 rate.

All the way through training, then, we're teaching what we consider to be stupid legs to do what we want them to do. Unfortunately, in Thoroughbred and Quarter Horse racing, very little time is spent on the basics of movement and agility during training. Dressage should be a part of every horse's schooling, and should continue throughout training. It's not done in racing, and some of the very important details of the racing gait are left out as well.

For example, lead changes. It is important, going into a turn during a high speed race, that the horse be on the left lead. Coming out of the turn, the horse should change back to the right lead in order to rest the left. Many horses will make these changes on their own, most of the time. But no time at all is spent teaching the horses cues for a lead change and few race riders know how to call for a lead change. This is a complex movement, involving two strides and precise timing - the animal needs to practice it every day. Yet, you can got to any racetrack in the country and watch dozens of horses coming around the turns on the wrong lead during morning exercises.

At maximum speeds, lead changes are not the easiest thing for a horse to accomplish, especially when in heavy traffic. Sometimes a jockey will jerk a horse left or right in the middle or at the beginning of a lead change. You can expect interference under these circumstances. Research has shown that a large percentage of racetrack breakdowns occur coming out of turns at about the point where a lead change would have occurred. Oftentimes there will be no lead change at all coming out of the final turn, and the trainer will later be heard to complain about the *horse* losing the race because he didn't change leads and became fatigued. Pard, you have to anticipate these problems before they occur.

Even if you want your racehorse schooled to improve his balance and coordination, you might not find anyone to do it for you. On the racetrack, there are so many horrific riding techniques that I was forced to produce a video, *Exercise Rider: The Good, The Bad, and The Ugly.* We have everything out there from "water skiers" to plain galloping sacks of manure. Worse, there is very little exercise being done in the morning - once around the racetrack is the norm. About five minutes a day to teach a million dollar athlete what he has to know to survive. A sad situation.

Chapter 17: More On Shoeing

Carl Lewis doesn't wear high heels, combat boots, clown shoes, side-weighted shoes, cowboy boots or slippers when he runs in practice or in competition. Why not? If you asked him, he'd probably say, "I'd kill myself in those." It's patently obvious to him that his feet are the most important part of his body when it comes to avoiding injury. Whatever forces are experienced by the foot are translated into stresses that are transferred all the way up the leg.

We play around a lot with the foot of the horse because it is the only place we think we can chop and cut and tack on and rebuild without crippling him. We're wrong. The horse weighs about five times what Carl Lewis weighs, travels twice as fast, and impacts the ground with a foot that is about the same size in square inches of contact surface. When we fool around with the feet of the horse, we're having a major impact on all the structures above it, including all the bones and joints of the leg up through the shoulder and hip, and tendons, ligaments and muscles. More performance horses are injured through poor shoeing than by any other single cause.

Let's talk about popular techniques and their possible consequences.

Weights: The weight of a shoe, and the distribution of that weight, is going to change the flight of the hoof through the air. More overall weight will cause more "action". In this case, action is essentially wasted effort, an unnecessarily high arc in the travel of the hoof, and a delay in the flight portion of the stride. When the foot hits the ground, you can expect higher concussion levels. this extra concussion will put pressure on the cannon bone and the cartilage and bones of the fetlock and knee joints. It will also tend to stress the deep flexor tendon and the check ligament. Use the lightest shoe that will get the job done.

Lateral Hoof Balance: We can also affect the way a hoof flies through the air by altering the length of hoof wall on either side of the foot. This can eliminate interference and make for a more efficient stride. But any time one side of the foot hits the ground before the other, there are two major problems to contend with. The long side of the foot hits first, taking most of the concussion of the stride on a small portion of the hoof wall. Quarter cracks can result, but the concussion is also transferred up the leg on that side, causing damage to cartilage in the joints, irritating or fracturing splint bones and changing other facets of stride mechanics.

The low side hits last, experiencing less concussion, but more stretch. The suspensory ligament takes the brunt of the punishment here, but the annular ligament suffers and the deep flexor tendon may experience constrictions that make it susceptible to a tear.

My advice is not to fool around with the lateral balance of the foot. If one front leg is hitting the other, you can use bandages to help spread them apart. If you've still got a knee knocker, think about replacing him on the roster - this guy is going to give you trouble of one kind or another. Rear/front interference is best handled by raising angles in front, lowering them behind, and shortening the toes in front. If that doesn't work, try squaring the toes in front.

Grabs, Trailers, Caulks: Anything that causes the foot, or a part of the foot, to come to a sudden stop is going to throw shock waves or twisting forces up the leg. The joints and the suspensories suffer most, but there is a possibility of cannon bone and tendon involvement with this kind of aggressive shoeing. Toe grabs, for example, have the effect of dropping the hoof angle by at least 2 degrees. Let's take a look at the conventional theory of toe grabs and critique it.

Racing horsemen feel that toe grabs on the front feet of racehorses allow them to grab ahold of the ground and pull themselves forward. The faster the horse has to go, the bigger the toe grabs. Racing Quarterhorses wear the biggest grabs of all.

In some circumstances, toe grabs on the rear feet may be useful, but grabs on the front simply bring on fatigue earlier while adding to the concussive and bending forces the forelegs must endure. The scientific truth is that the forelegs do not propel the horse forward and are there essentially to keep the horse's nose from plowing into the ground. Their job is to support the horse's body for a short portion of the stride and then roll over quickly and get out of the way so that the propulsive legs, the hind legs, can reach far up under the horse's body and grab hold of a nice chunk of real estate. Don't use toe grabs in front.

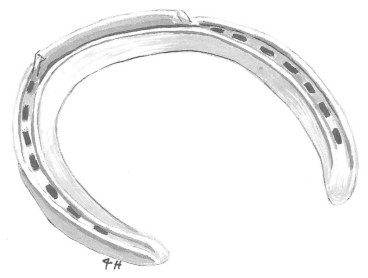

Toe grabs increase the rate that force is applied to the leg when the foot hits the ground - concussion.
(Illustration by Judy Hanson)

Pads, Degree Pads: Hoof pads can protect sensitive soles of sore-footed horses, but they have their unfortunate side effects. For one thing, they add weight to the foot, with some of the consequences outlined above. They also defeat the natural cupping of the horse's hoof, making it easier for the horse to slip on soft or sloppy surfaces.

Degree pads are a quick way of getting out of the Long Toe, Low Heel situation, but when combined with hoof alterations the farrier is likely to have made toward the same end, they can result in too dramatic a change at one time, leaving slack in the tendons and promoting the whipping action discussed elsewhere. Tendinitis and check ligament injury can result.

Rockered Toes: This technique is a step beyond rolled toes, where the foot itself is rounded off in front rather than simply hammering a rounded edge on the shoe. Unfortunately, the rockering process often results in instant hoof lameness because shoers who don't know what they're doing will cut into the sensitive layers of the hoof. This, in turn, can lead a horse to stay off the sore foot, putting excess pressure on the other leg. If the trainer doesn't notice and goes on with a tough workout, all sorts of nasty things can happen to the "good" leg.

Curled-Under Heels: In order to keep shoes from being pulled off by horses that are shod too long and low, the shoer will bend the ends of the shoe around under the bulbs of the heel. This will tend to contract the heels, and will also bruise the heels at the bulbs. Sore feet will eventually lead to other injuries if the situation is not corrected.

Shoes Too Small: For the sake of neatness and to save time, many shoers put on shoes that are too small and then rasp the horse's hoof down to fit. Big trouble on a number of counts. The hoof becomes smaller and contracted, subjecting itself and the rest of the leg to higher rates of injury. The hoof wall becomes thin, and cracks. The sole becomes bruised from contact with the shoe. As the foot grows, it overlaps the shoe, buttressing out, and the foot gradually becomes misshapen and unbalanced.

Pads Between Shoe and Hoof: The trouble here is that the nice cushion provided by the pad means that there is some squeeze to the pad, and that the shoe will move back and forth toward the foot, rubbing on the nails. The nails eventually wear through and part or all of the shoe pulls away. If the horse steps on a partially pulled shoe at a full gallop, he'll crack a coffin bone. If the shoe is flopping around, it's likely to catch a tendon, or pull away a quarter when it finally comes loose.

Plastic Cushion Between Shoe and Ground: This is an appropriate way to dampen the initial shock of impact without risking nail wear and early loss of the shoe. The only disadvantage may be that the shoe is heavier than normal. I've successfully raced both Standardbreds and Thoroughbreds on this type of shoe with no ill effects. I like them.

Rims and Swedges: A swedge is a "v" grooved into the shoe that picks up dirt and tends to make the hoof "stick" when it travels over the ground. Sometimes the metal rims on the outside of the swedge are accentuated, and sometimes the rims on the inside stick up higher. I have nothing against swedges except that they are a little more aggressive shoe than a plain flat plate - that means a little more shock goes up the leg upon impact. I prefer inside "rims" rather than outside, because the inside rim gives you a little bit of a rolled-toe effect. Both kinds of rims are far preferable to toe grabs or caulks.

LTLH: Elsewhere I've discussed the disaster that awaits a horse shod with LTLH. In the past, insulted farriers have written me to say that LTLH shoeing is just fine and that I should keep my opinions to myself, since they are unsupported by the research. They're wrong. The best researchers and clinicians in the world agree on this particular topic. Here's a sampling of their thoughts:

Dr. Doug Leach[1]: "The method of hoof breakover (the phase from heel liftoff to toe liftoff) influences the trajectory of foot flight. Hoof toe length influences timing of the liftoff of the heel in the final part of the stance phase: a lengthened toe delays and a shortened toe speeds the lifting of the heel (**Clayton**[2], 1987)."

Dr. Doug Leach[3]: "The navicular ligaments are tensed in normal horses as the hoof breaks over at the end of the stance phase and due to proportional changes of the phalanges that occur during weightbearing. These ligaments are also under excessive tension in horses with a conformation where the hoof wall-pastern axis is broken back, as when a horse has low or underrun heels. This type of conformation creates a chronic or long standing tension on the ligaments, which could mechanically restrict blood flow to and from the hoof.

"Dr. Chris Colles had induced navicular disease experimentally by cutting the heel down so that the hoof wall-pastern axis was broken back."

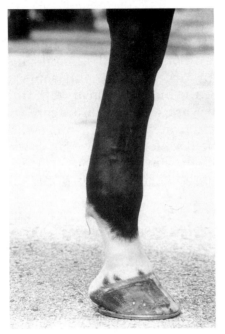

The underslung heel and low angle causes a broken-back hoof/pastern axis. There is also evidence of a bucked shin, or possibly a fracture, just below the knee.
(Photo by Suzie Oldham)

Dr. William Moyer[4]: "The foot remains the most common site of musculoskeletal problems in the athletic horse. Any number of problems can influence performance. The most common problems that the author diagnoses are:

1. Chronic subsolar bruising.
2. Low grade pedal osteitis in young horses.
3. Flat footed, long toe/low heel conformation."

Dr. William Moyer[5]: "The long toe in combination with a low heel is perhaps the most common and important foot shape abnormality seen. It is particularly prevalent in Thoroughbred racehorses, but it occurs in all horse types and breeds. The abnormal shape imposes abnormal forces on both the foot and the limb. This contributes theoretically to toe wall tearing, subsolar bruising, navicular disease, so called road founder, pedal osteitis, solar margin fractures, and hoof wall cracks. The long toe low heel prolongs foot breakover, suggesting that mechanically this would impose increased and prolonged tension on the digital flexor tendons and suspensory apparatus tissues. This may mechanically predispose the horse to navicular disease.

"The tendency in the racing industry is to maintain this shape, incorrectly expecting that it increases stride length and speed. Farriers are often encouraged or taught to place shoes that are 1/2 to a full size too small, to prevent the horse from pulling his or her shoes.

"The incidence of quarter cracks is quite high in feet that have low, underslung heels, in combination with a long toe and a flat sole."

Dr. William Moyer[6]: "Most horses (Clayton, Saskatoon) tend to land with their feet flat, as opposed to heel first or toe first. Toe length appears to be a critical factor in how the foot lands, as well as when it breaks over. Excessive toe length increases the tension on the suspensory apparatus at breakover. There is no advantage to a long toe, but there is obviously mechanical disadvantage."

Dr. George Maylin[7]: "See all those polo ponies? They're all Thoroughbreds donated to us because of 'incurable' navicular disease. We put heels back under them and they're all cured - must be 20 of them, some of them real expensive yearling purchases."

Dr. James R. Rooney[8]: "Why does the joint dorsiflex too much? There are several reasons: first, with hard work the animal becomes fatigued, the muscles cannot pull as much and the joint simply keeps moving, beyond its normal limit. Second, we put a weight, ourselves, on his back which increases the total load and hastens fatigue. Third, if the horses has a longish toe and a lowish heel, and many are trimmed that way, he will have more trouble raising his pastern during the second half of the stride which will lead to overdorsiflexion of the joint. We shall have more to say about that because the long toe, low heel business is associated with a number of other lameness problems in horses as well."

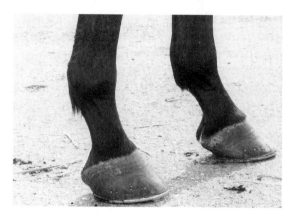

Pix # 22A, long toe and underslung heel

A longish toe and lowish heel.   The heel is underslung as well.   *(Photo by Suzie Oldham)*

Dr. William Jones[9]:   "Equine sports medicine has generated some controversy over the way a racehorse should be shod. The long-toe-low-heel trimming has been blamed by many veterinarians as the cause of much lameness seen at the track. Farriers and trainers who have shod and raced horses this way for years insist their way has been proven because so many winners have long toes and low heels. Many trainers have the idea that the long toe and low heel both increase stride and speed of the horse.

"Veterinarians studying biomechanics realize that as the toe gets longer and the heel gets lower the foot becomes placed further in front of the cannon bone. As a result, there is continual overextension of the fetlock, which places extra tension on the flexor support structures, increasing chances of bowed tendons. The longer toe forces the horse to have a greater arc to the foot flight, requiring more muscle control to flex the carpus, all of which leads to increased fatigue.

"The long toe interferes with normal toe breakover and leads to malformation of the foot, according to many veterinarians specializing in foot problems.   In the latest version of *Adams' Lameness in Horses*, Dr. Ted Stashak[10] says, 'The mechanical disadvantages created by this malconformation (LTLH) are many and include: 1) An increased overextension of the fetlock and carpus because the foot-landing position is forward of the ideal vertical axis. 2) The low, underslung heels markedly reduce the ability to absorb concussion. 3) The long toe makes breakover more difficult and tends to promote hoof wall tearing. 4) With time the back part of the hoof wall becomes weakened as a result of altered horn tubules growth and loss of the bars. 5) As much as a three-fold increase in concussion to the phalanges can occur because the pastern assumes a more upright position.' "

[1]Dr. Doug Leach, *Biomechanics of Limb Weightbearing*, Proc. Equine Lameness and Foot Conditions, University of Sydney Refresher Course for Veterinarians, published by Post Graduate Committee in Veterinary Science, 130, February,1990 (Syndey, N.S.W., Australia 2000).

[2]Dr. Leach makes reference to Dr. Hillary Clayton's paper presented before the American Association of Equine Practitioners in 1987 entitled "*Comparison of the stride of trotting horses trimmed with a normal and a broken-back hoof axis.*"

[3]Dr. Doug Leach, *Anatomy and biomechanics of the navicular bone, bursa and ligaments*, Proc. Equine Lameness and Foot Conditions, University of Sydney Refresher Course for Veterinarians, published by Post Graduate Committee in Veterinary Science, 130, February,1990 (Syndey, N.S.W., Australia 2000).

[4]Dr. William Moyer, *Obscure Lameness Affecting Performance*, ibid.

[5]Dr. William Moyer, *Pathogenesis of Foot Problems*, ibid.

[6]Dr. William Moyer, *Problems associated with Corrective Shoeing*, ibid.

[7]Dr. George Maylin, *personal communication.*

[8]Dr. James R. Rooney, The Lame Horse, (A. S. Barnes and Co., Inc., 1974) p. 89.

[9]Dr. William Jones, Sports Medicine for the Racehorse, (Veterinary data, Wildomar, CA, 1992) p.145.

[10]Dr. Ted Stashak, Adam's Lameness In Horses, (Lea & Febiger, Philadelphia, PA 1987)

Chapter 18: More Thoughts on Prevention

A good warmup prior to intense exercise can help you avoid soft tissue injury. If you are sitting in your easy chair reading this book, some 90% of your blood vessels are shut down and not carrying blood. The temperature of your muscles and tendons is relatively low. All this means that your tendons are not properly supplied with blood and they and their attached muscles are not as flexible as they would be if they'd just undergone some light exercise and become warmer.

What is a good warmup? Trot 1/2 mile to a mile, then go into a canter or lope for another 1 1/2 to 2 miles. What you want is a light sheen of sweat starting to form. In interval training, the first heat is also a warmup - the entire workout is warmed into, heat by heat, with the last heat the fastest. If your workout is going to include sudden starts or stops, or jumps, then you'll need to go into even more strenuous warmups to ensure that the body of the horse has its full range of motion available. A couple of accelerations, rolling into a quarter mile of significant speed, walking for a little bit, and rolling into another should be sufficient after the regular warmup. Walking the horse, before and after workouts, is virtually useless activity.

If you ask for speed or intense exercise before a horse is warmed up (a sheen of sweat is a good indicator of a warm horse) then the stretchability of the tendons is significantly less than the normal 8% we've talked about earlier. The flexibility of the joints is also compromised. So asking a cold horse for the kind of speed he did last week in a workout that was preceded by a good warmup is a big mistake. This happens every day to thousands of horses in Thoroughbred racing.

Warming down is a matter of continuing exercise immediately after strenuous exercise has been completed. Scientists say that the best warmdown takes place at 60% of the maximum heartrate seen during the bout of strenuous exercise. It's the first five minutes after hard work that is the most critical, and a warmdown lasting ten minutes appears to be ideal. The object is to help the muscles and surrounding tissues to pump out lactic acid and muscle cell debris that, if left alone, will cause muscle soreness and slow recovery. Walking a horse for hours after a race or workout is too little, too late for this purpose.

Weekend Warriors

The vast majority of performance and pleasure horses are owned and operated by folks who are not full-time horsefolk. That's fine. There's plenty of talent within those ranks. But you want to be aware of some athletic principles that apply to your particular situation involving conditioning, deconditioning, and basic care.

Just because you're not using your horse during the off season doesn't mean you can afford to ignore the rules of basic care during that time. This applies especially to the feet. If your horse is going to be off for a few months, pull the shoes immediately, trim up the foot, and then have the farrier come back for light trimming once every six weeks. During training and competition, the horse should be reshod or reset every four weeks. In addition, the hooves should be cleaned and inspected daily. That goes for the rest of his body, too. Look for cuts and infections. Look for signs of parasites, and be sure to be on a regular worming program. You can cut back the feed, but don't let the animal waste. And watch out for that thick lush grass in the paddock in the spring - grass founder!

A lot of the toughness you've built in the tendons during previous conditioning and competition will remain with the horse through months of time off. Over the years, there will be a cumulative effect and the tendons will gradually grow stronger with age. But, to an extent, the "use it or lose it" factor applies to the thickness and toughness of collagen-based tissues.

The deconditioning of the muscles is much more rapid and severe. First to go are the enzymes and fuels that enable sustainable speed. This can happen in a matter of weeks. Then, oxidative enzymes and mitochondria depopulate the unused muscle masses, compromising endurance. What's left after a few months of deconditioning is the "wiring", the neuromuscular coordination that enables the horse to call up millions of muscle cells simultaneously. Two months off, and you're essentially starting all over again - except you've got that fragile firepower waiting for an opportunity to explode. You've still got speed, but if you use it, you're going to run into a brick wall of fatigue very quickly. And there go the tendons.

Always start back easy and build intensity slowly. When you go back to work, go at it with volume first, then event-specific work, so that, until a few weeks before competition, the horse is always just a little tired. A little sleepy. A minimum of two workouts a week, of a half hour or longer of event-specific work, is necessary to maintain fitness for the sport.

Boots and Wraps

In general, the clean-legged horse is the best performer and is usually the best trained. Once the horse has developed agility and sure-footedness to perfection, the boots and protective wraps we've been using can often be taken off. You want to keep in mind that these devices can cause their own tendon problems, from chafing and mild tendinitis to a compression bow. There is hardly a protective device we can put on a horse's legs that is without a negative consequence.

Leather or plastic tendon boots offer rigid, effective protection from interference trauma. But they have weight, and weight interferes with an efficient stride. If speed is the primary goal, or if carrying speed for a distance is important, you just can't use these boots in competition. The same goes for rubber bell boots.

Polo bandages offer pretty fair protection from impact injuries, and so do straight cotton wraps. The disadvantages of these is that they can come unglued just at the wrong time, and in bad weather they tend to soak up water and mud and become very heavy.

Lighter leg wraps, like Vetrap™ and the 3M Equisport™ support bandage offer modest protection and support, but will have less of an impact on stride characteristics. While the Sport bandage is tougher than Vetrap, don't believe for a minute that you can slap it on a horse that is trying to bow and then go out and compete safely. The very best application I see for the Sport bandage is during exercise rehabilitation from a bow, when the exercise is light. During normal training, using a support bandage defeats the conditioning effect you're trying to develop in the tendons.

While there are a number of new products coming into the equine market being advertised as "support bandages" or "sports medicine boots," these devices are of doubtful use in either preventing bowed tendons or as a tool during rehabilitation. On the one hand, it is unlikely that these bandages and boots will provide much protection for tendons during exercise, and it is questionable whether you even want to exercise a horse that needs such support. In my mind, these tendon supports offer a false sense of security and encourage going back to work too soon after a tendon injury.

The only exception may be rundown patches. Any horse that is coming back with dirt or grass stains on his fetlock should wear rundowns during hard work and competition. Stick-on rundown patches are the best approach here. You can also try to raise the angles in front so that his breakover is less delayed.

Chapter 19: Intervention

Intervention is the process of detecting oncoming lameness, determining and eliminating the cause, and allowing and encouraging complete healing before going on with the horse's training. It would be ideal if we could take all the precautions necessary to prevent tendon injury, but most of us are going to be faced with oncoming tendon problems from time to time, no matter how careful we are in avoiding the circumstances that lead to them

Sometimes you just can't outsmart Mother Nature and you find yourself confronted with the "start of something bad." If, like most racetrack trainers, you simply ignore those early signs and go on with the horse until big trouble appears, you've lost your golden opportunity to intervene in an oncoming lameness. Lost your chance to dodge a deadly bullet. Lameness intervention is far less expensive than rehabilitation.

Lameness intervention has four steps: detecting oncoming injury early, complete diagnosis, eliminating the cause, and carefully reintroducing exercise stresses. Each step is equally important, but the first is obviously critical.

Detection

Don't cover up what you're supposed to detect. Bowed tendons seldom happen all at once, although the severe injury seems to happen suddenly. Part of the reason for this is that we fool ourselves with wraps, bandages, liniments, and poultices. Minor inflammation and swelling tends to go unnoticed with horses that are "kept tight" with overnight bandages (and sometimes these bandages cause a bow all by themselves). The first step, then, in detecting oncoming tendinitis or bows is to leave the legs alone overnight unless you're actually treating an injury.

Paints, blisters, and drugs will also mask the symptoms of oncoming tendon trouble. For example, if you notice some filling down around the ankle and decide to give the horse a dose or two of Bute, the swelling will go away, there will be no pain for the horse, and you'll conclude that, whatever the problem was, it's gone now. Anybody who has worked with equine athletes knows that these little exercise intolerances pop up all the time, and they tend to go away as quickly as they appeared. If you call in a vet and an ultrasound machine every time you encounter a little of this and that, you'll go broke before you ever get the horse into competition. A better approach is to do nothing medical for the affected area. Instead, cut the workload in half for a few days, leave the legs open, and watch what happens. If the heat or swelling persists, or gets worse, then call in the vet for an ultrasound examination.

The least serious condition is generalized filling. Filling, or stocking up, is a thickness from the fetlock up 1/3 to 1/2 of the cannon bone. The valley between the superficial digital flexor tendon and the cannon bone is filled and thickened tightly with fluid. There may or may not be heat, depending on the cause and the thickness of the filling. In young horses, this can result from too much exercise too soon. The blood vessels must strengthen and become elastic enough that their backwash valves can keep fluids from sinking back into the lower leg when the horse is standing. Older horses standing still can get the same symptoms. Cut the work in half until the filling is gone, then slowly sneak back through the old work level.

Another kind of filling can take place if there's an infection below the joint, as in "scratches" behind the pastern or a hoof infection. Indeed, you can make the whole lower leg look like a shipwreck by applying the wrong sauce to the legs or ankles. These sauces don't do any good - just avoid them. Instead, spend the time saved from not rubbing and wrapping legs thinking about and designing more judicious exercise protocols. Or watching the shoer, to make sure he doesn't do something stupid.

You don't want to confuse filling or stocking up with an injury to the deep digital flexor tendon or suspensory, though. At the ankle, there are a lot of things going on, and all sorts of organs are passing through some narrow spaces. Injuries to the deep digital flexor tendon can appear to be ankle or suspensory problems, and a severe suspensory pull can at first appear to be stocking up. Except: it's hot, it's one-legged and one-sided on the leg, it begins low on the cannon bone and spreads upward - stocking seems to happen overnight and goes well up the leg before you have a chance to recognize it.

As you slide your fingers down the superficial flexor tendon, you should be able to distinctly feel the parts of the underlying tissues, the deep flexor and the suspensory ligament. There should be no mushiness at all, none anywhere along the superficial digital flexor tendon, or beneath the superficial digital flexor tendon. No thickening. No hot spots. Your grip should be tight enough that going over a soreness will cause the horse to flinch. No heat at the sesamoids, none behind the pastern. In general, any trouble that begins showing up on the flexor side of the leg, that is, behind the cannon bone or pastern, or at the sesamoids, can be considered a threat to bow. That's because many of the parts of the flexor apparatus come under stress at the same time as the tendon - particularly the sesamoids and the XYV ligaments behind the pastern. The cause for their distress is likely to be the cause for the eventual bow. If any signs of distress are evident, cut out all strenuous work for a few days, and cut the overall workload to half. Anything that persists, you should worry about.

An injury to the deep digital flexor tendon is hard to diagnose because it usually occurs right where it could be confused with a suspensory problem or wind puffs - low, just above the fetlock. However, if you've run your fingers tightly down the inside of the superficial digital flexor tendon, you'll feel all three organs, the superficial digital flexor tendon, the deep digital flexor tendon, and the suspensory, all the way down. If the deep digital flexor tendon is injured, there will be a bump on it. If the suspensory is injured, the joint capsule itself will probably be swollen, at least toward the rear of the joint, and the swelling will distend below the joint. The suspensory usually has its trouble where it connects with the annular ligament that wraps around the joint.

Of course, any bumps on the superficial digital flexor tendon or deep digital flexor tendon call for an immediate ultrasound. If you look sideways at the superficial digital flexor tendon and it's not absolutely straight, bring in the ultrasound sector scanner. If you discover a thickness up by the check ligament, take an ultrasound series.   Any thickness just above and to the rear of the fetlock - take some pictures. These are signs of big trouble on the way and you'd better not try to rub or squeeze them down or medicate them away and go on with the horse.

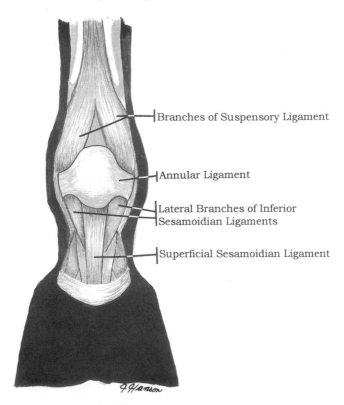

Branches of Suspensory Ligament

Annular Ligament

Lateral Branches of Inferior Sesamoidian Ligaments

Superficial Sesamoidian Ligament

Here you see the ligaments on the back of the pastern, completing the suspensory apparatus which holds the fetlock off the ground. Damage to these ligaments usually occurs from the same stresses that injure the flexor tendons or the suspensory ligament.

(Illustration by Judy Hanson)

If the source of heat or swelling is other than at or near the superficial digital flexor tendon and deep digital flexor tendon, you probably don't have a tendon injury, yet. Get out your *Adams' Lameness in Horses* and study the anatomy of the area showing signs. Read what Adams says about the possible problems associated with the body part. The best treatment for inflammation is reduced workload and the application of cold therapy. See what you can get done in that direction while you figure out what caused the problem. If you're stymied, call in the vet - the one with an ultrasound machine. Even if the vet decides that an ultrasound investigation is not necessary, he'll be the best judge of whether there is any tendon involvement. Remember that swelling within the fetlock joint can put a lot of pressure on the deep flexor tendon and irritate the sheath of the superficial flexor tendon.

Horse Talk

Another sign, this one from the horse: the animal with oncoming tendon problems will try to find ways to "rest" his tendons. His gait may change, with his rear end coming farther up under him at the trot and canter. A horses with sore tendons doesn't like to trot fast - he'll go into a canter when you ask for an extended trot. He'll tend to "prance" in front. He won't like to turn in tight circles. Back at the stall, he'll dig holes and then stand on the edges of the holes, his heels elevated, to rest the flexor apparatus.

When a horse has just experienced a tendon tear, the injured leg is likely to shake as he tries to stand on it - get him to the barn and break out the ice. He may point with the injured leg, but if he stands wide with it, he's probably got a knee injury (most likely, a chip at the third metacarpal). Of course, a horse will point a sore foot, too.

Oddly enough, unless the animal has a severe bow, you won't see much in the way of nodding at the trot. Somehow a bow doesn't produce a lot of "three-legged" lameness unless it's very severe. However, yesterday's enthusiastic, "let's go" athlete will suddenly calm down. Fillies and mares will tend to go off feed, while geldings and colts will tend to sulk. All will tend to get a little cranky. But these are signs that could accompany any oncoming problem.

Heat

The very best early warning system I have encountered is the infrared thermometer or infrared thermography. Infrared light is put out by objects that are warm to any degree at all. The intensity of this light can be measured as temperature - from a distance. As far as heat is concerned, a degree and a half, Centigrade, is significant. That is, if one part of a tendon is 1.5 degrees or more hotter than the same location on the other tendon, you've got an active inflammatory response that should be looked into. At 4 or 5 degrees, where the hand can actually feel the differences, you've already done significant damage. This same warning applies to differences in temperature along the tendon itself - the heat should be uniform the entire length of the tendon.

Now, inside the superficial digital flexor tendon, where the deep digital flexor tendon and the suspensory ligament travel, is a little valley that also contains blood vessels. This area is always a degree or two warmer than the outside of the superficial digital flexor tendon. However, no part of the leg, up past the knee, should be warmer than the coronary band of the hoof. If you find excessive heat in the rear of the fetlock or behind the pastern, tendon trouble is possible in the future.

Infrared thermometers are available for under $1,000 - you want to get the ones that display the actual temperature in tenths of a degree. Infrared thermography gives you real-time pictures of the heat patterns of your horse, but these systems are expensive - the one I use, the Hughes Probeye, costs $33,000. With this machine, I produced a video tape called *Heat Patterns in Lame or Coming Lame Horses*. Purchasers of this book can buy the tape from the Russell Meerdink Company for $29.95.

Complete Diagnosis

If you still have some heat or swelling that fails to disappear after minor adjustments to training, then you have to go further with your diagnosis. Two modalities are useful: ultrasound sector scanning and X-ray. Ultrasound is the "X-ray of soft tissues." You'll want to know if there is any damage to the tendons or their sheaths and, if so, where it is and what the extent of the damage is. If you can't find tendon or suspensory damage, then X-rays will help you look at cartilage and bone.

Diagnosis of an injury includes, or should include, its "etiology," or cause. It's not enough to diagnose a bow, treat it, then go back into the same conditions that caused it in the first place. The horse's recent history will play a large part in determining exactly how a tendon was injured. You should be keeping records of every godlike thing you do with each animal. The exercise, the topical applications, groom and rider comments, equipment changes, training surface changes, shoeing changes, etc. The more information you can give the vet, the more likely he is to detect injuries that may not be readily apparent - and it might enable the vet to give a more accurate prognosis for rehabilitation. In fact, you may find that what you think is a bow is something else entirely. A check ligament injury, for example, can look like a high bow, but is far less serious. "Mud fever" blows up the whole leg, but is just a fungus that, when properly treated, allows the leg to return to normal very quickly. Several topical applicants can cause the same kind of reaction in some horses.

Eliminating the Cause

Bowed tendons are not accidents; they happen for a reason. They're a function of improper biomechanics. Far more often than not, these improper mechanics are human-engineered. I can't tell you how many times I've seen racehorses rebowed simply because their trainers started back too early with them and then put them through the same process that injured them in the first place.

Oftentimes there are subtle causes for injuries that require time and though to unearth, and then, quite a bit of effort to avoid the next time around. Throughout this book, I've listed many of the ways you can cause a horse to bow.

These unfortunate techniques don't just apply to racehorses. Even if one or another of them is not exactly what you've done to your horse, you'll find plenty of hints here as to exactly why your horse has injured a tendon. The very first question you want to ask yourself when you see an injured tendon is, "How did I bow this horse?" Not "Why did this horse bow on me?" Once you've figured it out, then you have to take all the steps necessary to avoid doing the same thing again - to this horse, or to any other horse in the barn.

The three most likely causes: improper shoeing, sudden increases in speed without adequate preparation, fatigue. The least likely cause: a "rap." Remember, don't just focus on what the horse did today that made the bow show up today. A bow can show up as many as three days after the injury actually occurred (that's a good sign of a modest injury - but it's a bow nonetheless). The chart on the next page tells how to avoid all the more common causes.

Rules For Avoiding Bowed Tendons:

◆ No sudden increases in speed.
◆ When changing surfaces, take several days of moderate work on the new surface before bringing the horse up to speed.
◆ No speed for at least three days after a shoeing change.
◆ Avoid Long Toe, Low Heel shoeing. Avoid toe grabs, especially in front. Never make more than a 2 degree angle change per shoeing.
◆ Avoid fatigue at all stages of training.
◆ Lay down some serious miles before moving on to the more intense work.
◆ Learn to recognize accidents waiting to happen - like hot walking machines and sleepy, cranky grooms.
◆ Heed your horseman's early warning system. Find out what's wrong, eliminate the cause, then slowly bring the horse back.
◆ Use whatever science you can to monitor your animal's progress.
◆ Try to determine the individual horse's work/ recovery cycle.
◆ Supplement with antioxidants.
◆ Introduce new skills gradually, and practice them until they're perfect - but don't try to get it all done in one day.
◆ After a "breakthrough" workout, where unexpected speed suddenly arrives, skip the next scheduled hard workout.
◆ Keep track of all the details, the workouts, the nutrition, the shoeing numbers, the horse's behavior, any medical attention necessary, observations from the handlers.
◆ Believe the horse when he says he's hurt; never believe him when he says he's Godzilla.
◆ Warmup for at least 2 1/2 miles, or 15 minutes, before performing any strenuous work.

Rebuilding

The final stage of intervention is the rebuilding of the injured athlete. If you've intervened properly, before the injury is severe, then exercise rehabilitation is going to be the treatment of choice. Earlier, I outlined the type of exercise that is likely to encourage proper healing of a bowed tendon. But remember, tendons require Tincture of Time.

Here's a clue: when the tendon looks absolutely normal, not a sign of the bow you had months ago, you still have a long way to go to rebuild a tendon that is capable of the kind of performance you were asking for when the bow originally happened - even if you've eliminated what you believe to be the cause. Ultrasound scans every 30 to 60 days are the only way to be sure that the tendon is healing. And four months of careful, progressively loaded exercise following a clean ultrasound is not over-cautious.

Remember, the rehabilitation process begins with first aid, limiting the damage. Once the tendon is beginning to heal, light exercise, starting with a lot of controlled walking (not just throwing the horse out into the paddock) begins to accelerate healing while directing the tendon fibers to form themselves in line to the stresses they'll later experience. Gradually, step by step, month after month, higher intensity exercises are added, with close attention paid to the injured tendon every day. Work should progress from long and slow to shorter, faster exercises. Avoid the "surprises" that produced the bow in the first place.

Epilogue

Once-bowed horses can fare very well in less stressful events without ever rebowing if properly rehabilitated. That is, race horses can become eventers and show horses, jumpers can become endurance horses and pleasure horses. There are dozens of athletic careers for good horses that are not nearly as stressful as the ones that cause bows.

The problem with trying to bring a bowed racehorse back to racing or jumping is that it's a nearly impossible task and, if you are able to race the horse again, his career is likely to be short and unproductive. I know, there are cases where once-bowed horses went on to win Stakes races, but these are rare indeed, and the more likely result is a horse that becomes so severely injured that he must be put down. There is a point at which your humanity must stop you from attempting to squeeze the very last drop of productive blood from your horse. It would be pleasant for me if one result of this small book is to persuade you that the stopping point is far short of having to call the meat man.

On the other hand, I can only encourage you to allow your injured horse to become all that he can be in a less stressful arena. This is genuine rehabilitation, where the animal becomes useful again, earns his keep, becomes a source of pride and happiness for you.

The equine athlete is not a four-legged domesticated beast of burden. He's a Spirit, an Angel, upon whose wings our hearts are lifted far beyond our own Earthbound, plodding limits. He's a Gift, well worthy of respect, care, and a certain reverence reserved for those things that are noble in Nature. There are few undertakings in life as gratifying as doing the right thing by your horse. This is one creature that pays back tenfold.

Sportsmedicine Glossary

From now on, in all my books, I'm going to include an expanding glossary of words and concepts that are central to the understanding of applied science in the conditioning of horses. In the text of my books, I generally explain most concepts fully, once. But then I tend to refer to previously discussed terms as though my readers are familiar with them. Now, you can jump into the glossary when you run into a concept you don't fully understand, and if necessary, refer to the Index to take you to the areas of the book where the concept is being used in context.

I'd suggest you read this glossary as though it were another chapter. Think of it as "key concepts". Not all terms defined here will be in this book - some will be introduced in later works. Don't try to memorize, just read it quickly straight through. One more quick exposure to these ideas won't hurt a bit.

Abduction: Moving a body part away from the midline of the body.

Abscess: Microbes, leukocytes, and liquefied tissue debris walled off by fibroblasts (a certain cell that gives rise to connective tuissues) and collagen.

Absorption: Movement of materials across a layer of epithelial cells from a body cavity or compartment toward the blood.

Accelerations: These are workouts similar to the Fartlek ("speed play") workout originally developed in Sweden. Leland Stanford's big deal was accelerations or "brushes" with Standardbreds. Essentially, you move around the track at a modest pace, then bolt into a sprint, then pull back to the modest pace, then repeat the process several times over three or four continuous miles. These workouts are known for opening up the strides of Standardbreds. They're not so hot with Thoroughbreds or Quarter Horses because these animals are hard to control through a series like this.

Acclimatization: An adaptive change caused by environmental stimuli. Horses moving from hot to cold, or cold to hot environments need time to acclimatize before undergoing stress. The fitter the animal, the less acclimatization necessary - that is, environmental stressors have a lesser effect.

Acid: a chemical compound capable of releasing Hydrogen ions to a solution. A Base picks up H ions. Lactic acid (acid) and sodium bicarbonate (base) neutralize each other.

Acidosis: Elevated hydrogen ions in the arterial blood (usually as a consequence of lactic acid). A horse that blows for a long time after a race probably has acidosis - but in hot climates, blowing can indicate high body temperatures.

Acquisition: The ability to acquire fitness when exposed to appropriate exercise. Some horses have high rates of acquisition while others struggle under heavy workloads just to attain small increases in athletic ability. Acquisition can be specific, that is, one horse may gain the ability to make speed quickly, while he'll struggle to gain endurance or stamina. Acquisition is essentially determined by genetics.

Adduction: Movement of a body part toward the midline of the body.

Aerobic/Anaerobic: With oxygen/without oxygen. As exercise intensity increases, muscle fuel burning switches from oxidative to enzymatic, aerobic to anaerobic, and fatiguing lactic acid is produced as a bi-product of the anaerobic process.

ACTH: Adrenocorticotropic hormone. The master hormone that triggers most glands to secrete other body controlling hormones. Real popular with racehorse trainers and veterinarians. In some cases it's a substitute for a tranquilizer, in others, it's supposed to be a "hop".

Actin: The contractile protein in muscles that binds to myosin cross bridges in muscle filaments.

Adenosine Triphosphate: ATP. The major energy carrier - reduces to Adenosine Diphosphate (ADP) + energy. Some vets and trainers have suggested that injecting ATP I.V. improves performance.

Adipose Tissues: Fat-storing tissues. A racehorse carries very little fat in his body as adipose tissue, most of it around the liver.

Afferents: Extensions of nerve cells bringing messages into the nerve cell or toward the brain. Efferents carry messages away. There is continuous 2-way communication within nerve cells in order to adjust their activities to what is happening in other parts of the body. For example, the appearance of lactic acid in the bloodstream will cause sensors to call on certain nerves to increase heartrate and respiration rate.

Agonist Muscles: Muscles that contract to produce a movement. Antagonist muscles must relax in order to allow a movement to occur. Training (practice) allows for a more coordinated relationship between agonists and antagonists - efficiency of motion is the result.

Alkalosis: Reduced hydrogen ion concentration in arterial blood - as can happen with a blowing horse (blowing off heat) that is hyperventilating. Common in endurance horses.

Ambient: Environmental - as in ambient temperature.

Amino Acid: A molecule containing an amino group, a carboxyl group, and a side chain all attached to a single carbon atom. Amino acids (there are 20) are the components of body proteins and are known by their side chains.

Ammonia: Substance produced during the breakdown of amino acids - converted in the liver to urea. Evidence of tissue breakdown. Some consider serum ammonia a better indicator of exercise intensity and stress than lactic acid.

Anaerobic Threshold: As exercise intensity increases, work is performed increasingly via the anaerobic pathway. But at a certain point, lactic acid production increases geometrically - "goes out the roof". Scientists have set this "anaerobic threshold" at a blood lactate concentration of 4 millimoles per liter. In the unfit horse, the anaerobic threshold is typically reached at heartrates of 180+. In very fit horses, the anaerobic threshold can be stretched past 200+ heartrates. Racehorses reach and survive lactic acid concentrations of from 16 mmole to 40 mmole, but concentrations of 20 mmole or more can be dangerous due to the resulting fatigue and injury potential. (See also aerobic.)

Anabolic: A chemical that inhibits the breakdown (catabolism) of protein. Anabolic steroids cause an increase in muscle mass by shutting down muscle protein catabolism. Normally, a two-way anabolism/catabolism is ongoing in most body tissues.

Anemia: A low red cell count, as far as most vets are concerned. In fit horses, the spleen stores away a higher percentage of red cells for reinjection into the blood stream at a time of high exercise demand. This sign of fitness can easily be misdiagnosed as anemia. The true test for anemia is Serum Ferritin. Unless the vet has performed that test, he has no business diagnosing anemia and injecting Vitamin B and Iron.

Analgesia: Pain inhibition.

Androgenic: Produces male characteristics. An undesirable side effect of some anabolic steroids.

Anomaly: Deviation from the norm. A horse like Secretariat is an anomaly of racehorse genetics. The central premise of true genetics is "regression to the norm". That is, breed a Secretariat to a champion female and the resulting foal will likely display the athletic prowess of the families of those superhorses, not

171

a combination of their individual natural abilities. If you "breed the best to the best and hope for the best", you'll have a long wait. Here's something interesting, though. Some scientists are suggesting that athletic ability is passed from mother to son, father to daughter. Thus, daughters of Secretariat should do better than his sons.

Anorexia: Lack of appetite or aversion to food. Most sore horses display anorexia to one degree or another. In some, it can become a long-term problem, and trainers tend to look for an anabolic steroid with androgenic effects as a solution. Equipoise is the brand most often chosen. Other solutions include three days of 2 grams of bute, every other day injections of Ace, and B vitamin/arsenic combinations.

Anoxia: Lack of oxygen. All racehorses, and many other performance horses, suffer from anoxia during or after some parts of their competitive events.

Anterior: Toward the front.

Antibiotic: Fights bacterial infection.

Antihistamine: Fights swelling caused by histamine release following injury or irritation of tissues.

Antagonist Muscles: See agonist muscles

Anti-inflammatory: Fights inflammation.

Antioxidants: Chemicals like Vitamins E & C, beta-carotene, Selenium, and SOD prevent the wholesale tissue destruction by free radicals after hard work, disease, and injury.

Apnea: Cessation of respiration. Sprinting horses sometimes suffer from apnea during the first strides out of the gate. It is believed that Quarterhorses sometimes run an entire race apneic (without breathing).

Applied Research: Research that deals with solving real-world problems. As opposed to basic research, which investigates "what God hath wrought". Accidental spills in basic research laboratories sometimes result in miraculous cures and inventions. Applied researchers spill stuff accidentally on purpose. The equine industries need more applied researchers - and funding for them.

Arthroscopic: Interior views of joints provided by an arthroscope - generally used in viewing surgical repair of joints.

Arrhythmia: Any variation from normal heartbeat rhythm. Athletes are known for a variety of arrhythmias.

Artery: Thick-walled, elastic vessel that carries blood away from the heart.

Artifact: An artificially-produced occurrence. When a heartrate monitor electrode is loosely applied, or a wire is flapping, erratic heartrates can be seen on the monitor, such as a sequence like 130, 197, 245, 128, 128, 175 - all while the horse is loping at a steady speed. This is an artifact, not a genuine heartrate reading.

Asymmetry: Both sides are not the same. In the horse, asymmetrical legs lead to inefficient strides, higher heartrates, and injury. The primary cause of asymmetrical legs is sloppy shoeing.

Atrium: A chamber of the heart that receives blood from the veins and passes it on to the ventricle on the same side of the heart.

Atrophy: Wasting away of tissue - as in injured muscles and muscles whose nerves have been severed.

Autonomic Nervous System: Involuntary control system for heartrate, digestive functions, respiration, vascular tone. While this efferent division of the peripheral nervous system is not voluntarily controlled, it still reacts quickly to situations the body encounters. For example, when a horse begins a hard exercise, the autonomic nervous system shifts blood and body fluids away from the intestines and out into the working muscle groups. Its sympathetic and parasympathetic divisions innervate cardiac muscle, smooth muscle, and glands.

Axon: Nerve fiber.

Azoturia: Tying up. Muscle cramping.

Background Mileage: All properly designed conditioning programs begin with background or base mileage. This entails building a daily exercise regime of Long Slow Distance work. With interval training programs we refer to horses coming off a 6-mile base or a 4-mile base. This refers to the fact that the animal is exercising 6 continuous galloping miles (or jogging miles, in the case of Standardbreds) every day. Once this background mileage is established, the animal can move on to more strenuous, event-specific exercise. The idea is to toughen the structural systems before going on to higher intensity work.

Bacteria: The simplest of nongreen vegetable organisms. Bacteria are vital for digestion in man and horse, and products are available to resupply digestive bacteria to horses that have lost them due to overheating.

Baroreceptor: A receptor sensitive to pressure and rate of change of pressure. Arterial baroreceptors respond to mean arterial pressure and pulse pressures, helping to regulate heart rate and blood vessel diameters. Drugs like Lasix and Clenbuterol override these automatic actions.

Bilateral: Both sides. Bilateral tendon swelling is a double bow.

Bilirubin: A yellow substance resulting from the breakdown of heme (the iron-containing component of hemoglobin) in red blood cells. High levels indicate oncoming anemia.

Biomechanics: The laws of mechanics as applied to living things. Lack of knowledge about the biomechanics of racehorses leads to thousands of injuries.

Blood Lactate Concentration: Actually, blood lactic acid concentration. Lactic acid is a weak acid that is continually attracting and throwing off hydrogen ions. Separated from its hydrogen ion, it's lactic acid; with its hydrogen ion intact, it's lactate. The acid state is the problem, since it lowers the blood and muscle pH and causes fatigue. As mentioned above, lactic acid concentration is measured in millimoles per liter of blood plasma. At rest, the horse will carry less than 1 mmole per liter.

Bog Spavin: A fluid-filled distention low and inside on the hock. Similar to wind puffs in the ankle, the bog spavin is not an injury of itself, but suggests unusual activity within the joint. It's a blemish that most often goes away when the problems within the joint have been resolved. Both are referred to as idiopathic (don't know where it came from) synovitis (inflammation of the synovial capsule).

Bolus: A lump of food that has been chewed and mixed with saliva.

Bone Density: The measurement of the mineral content of bone. Recent science suggests that higher bone density indicates increased bone strength, and that bone density increases with with introduction of higher and higher levels of concussion. But beware: this is not true of cartilage. Increasing concussion too rapidly, in order to develop strong bone, will leave the cartilage behind - you may avoid bucked shins, but you'll have ankles and kness to contend with. Best bet: a gradual introduction to speed.

Bone Spavin: Usually occuring on the inside of the hock, these are bony cysts that form with osteoarthritis. It is thought that ultrasound treatment can reduce the size of these cysts, but this treatment should be reserved for technicians who know how to use the more sophisticated ultrasound devices, like Mimi Porter of Lexington.

Bucked Shins: When stress hits the cannon bone too quickly, as when speed is suddenly introduced to a horse that has only been slow galloping, remodeling will begin. If the bone experiences more of the same before it has had a chance to strengthen, then bucked shins will result. Bucked shins can be anything from an irritated periosteum to actual fractures in the cannon bone. They can be avoided completely.

Buffering: Neutralizing acid by the introduction of a base. Blood buffering: creating a temporary basic condition in the blood so that lactic acid is buffered when it appears during intense exercise.

Bursa(ae): "A closed sac with a cellular membrane resembling a synovial membrane which is interposed between moving parts, or at points of unusual pressure such as between bony prominences and tendons." (Adams') A kind of protective padding that can become painfully inflamed, as in tennis elbow or navicular bursitis.

Calcification: When a tissue other than bone develops bony characteristics. For example, injecting corticosteroids into joints and tendons tends to cause calcification of cartilage and tendon tissue. Big trouble.

Calorie: Amount of heat needed to raise 1 gram of water 1 degree C.

Cannon Bone: The third metacarpal bone.

Capillary: The smallest of the blood vessels - a single layer of endothelial cells through which pass water, nutrients, dissolved gases, and wastes.

Carbohydrate: A substance composed of atoms of carbon, hydrogen, and oxygen - sugars and starches. This is the only viable source of fuel for the racehorse.

Cardiac: Of the heart.

Cardiac Output: The volume of blood pumped by each ventricle per minute.

Cardiovascular Center: A group of neurons in the brainstem medulla which serves as a major integrating center for reflexes affecting heartrate, cardiac contractility, vascular resistance, and vascular capacity in the control of blood pressure.

Cardiovascular System: The heart, lungs, blood, and blood vessels - and their controlling mechanisms.

Carpal Canal: Behind the knee there is a channel that provides passage for the lateral digital extensore muscle and its synovial sheath. The carpal canal lies in a critical intersection of the knee joint and some of the problems of the knee can be reflected in swelling and heat that follows along the carpal canal, to the rear and slightly below the knee. This can look like a check ligament problem but is indicative of knee joint problems. I've seen this inflammation on thermographs of Standardbred knees many times.

Carpus: The knee of the horse - the wrist in humans.

Cast: The horse lies down too close to the wall of his stall, rolls over towards the wall, and finds himself with no leg purchase to get out of the position - like a turtle on its back. Then comes much flailing about and possible serious injury. Building up the bedding around the outside of the stall can help prevent this situation.

Back in the good old days, part of the breaking process was called "casting", where the trainer threw the horse to the ground by way of ropes and leverage several times so that the animal woud come to realize who was boss. This still goes on in some circles, but not with racehorses - for the most part.

The saddest, and funniest, horse video I've ever seen was a promotional video for a training center where the trainer was demonstrating how to cure a racehorse from bolting, or running away with the rider. The tape showed a month of a variety of arena exercises where the trainer attached ropes to one or more of the horse's legs, casting it to the ground, over and over again, as the voiceover expounded upon the psychological aspects of this method. Unbelieveable. The horse appeared to, finally, calm down and give in. Then came the final test - under saddle in a large paddock. Things start out ok, with the rider passing by the video camera with a big smile on his face. But the video ends with an out-of-control animal, bucking, kicking and running like hell right at the camera, with a wide-eyed, wide-mouthed rider screaming "Whoa!" There is justice in this world.

Catabolic: A breakdown of chemical structures and tissues.

Center of Gravity: The point of perfect balance in the body. The rider of the horse must be balanced over the center of gravity of the horse. The center of gravity will move backwards if the animal is properly fed and exercised.

Central Fatigue: When sensors out on the periphery of the body pick up chemical and mechanical signs of overstress, messages are sent back to the Central Nervous System. In turn, the CNS will lower its demands on the firing muscle cells. The result is that the racer slows down. Central fatigue may contribute as much as 50% of speed loss at the end of a race.

Central Nervous System: The brain and spinal cord, and associated components.

Curvilinear Relationship: Not a straight line. If you draw a graph of heartrate versus speed, you'd get a linear relationship, but if you drew a graph of speed versus lactic acid concentration, then, at the anaerobic threshold, the graph for lactic acid would begin to curve upward, increasing much faster than speed increases.

Chronic Injury: An injury that takes a long time to produce and a long time to heal.

Circadian Rhythm: The body's biological clock. You can determine you animal's circadian rhythm by monitoring heartrate and body temperature around the clock - over a period of 48 hours. During periods of high metabolism, the athlete is a better performer. Circadian rhythms can be fooled and manipulated. Racehorses would do better training at the time of day that they're going to race, not early in the morning.

Clustered Workouts: A short series of closely-spaced workouts tends to produce a faster racehorse - for a short period of time. Sometimes, though, the horse will have found a new plateau and will continue to race at the new speed for some time. Clusters are typically 3-4 workouts spaced two to three days apart. Some Standardbreds and Thoroughbreds have successfully performed clusters that were run every day for three days.

Collagen: Fibrous strength-giving component of connective tissues.

Complementary Lameness: When an original lameness goes undetected or unresolved and a secondary lameness occurs, sometimes more severe than the first, because the horse throws stress away from the original area and onto another leg or another location on up the leg.

Concussion: Compression stresses caused by impact. In horses, as speed increases, concussive forces playing upon the feet, bones of the lower leg, and the cartilage pads between them, increase, sometimes to the point of failure of these structures. A gradual introductiuon to concussion will allow all tissues to adapt. Certain kinds of shoes, and certain track surfaces, attenuate concussion, preventing injury.

Conformation: The alignment of the various parts of the horse's body. There are defects in conformation that will limit athletic performance and predispose the animal to injury. The best book concerning conformation and lameness is *Adams' Lameness In Horses*. This book comes in two formats, one abridged. Buy the big book.

Congenital Defects: Inborn, sometimes inbred, defects or faults in conformation or physiology.

Connective Tissues: Tendons, ligaments, fascia.

Contracted Heels: A horse shod with the Long Toe, Low Heel configuration will eventually develop contracted or pinched heels. As the hoof narrows behind, circulation is compromised and navicular disease and false navicular symptoms will appear.

Contraction Time: The time interval between the stimulus and the development of peak tension by a muscle. While fast twitch muscle cells have a shorter contraction time than slow twitch cells, when the FT cells get low on fuel, their contraction time slows. In fact, some studies suggest that a 35% fuel depletion in FT cells will casue a significant slowing in FT contraction times.

Contralateral: Diagonally opposite legs, as in left front, right hind.

Core Temperature: Deep body temperature. Core temperature is monitored by the hypothalamus, and deviations from the norm will cause adjustments - blowing, shivering, closure or opening of skin vasculature, etc. I've seen core temperatures higher than 108 degrees after some interval workouts - with no ill effects. Stresses like this help the horse to tolerate hot weather racing.

Coronary Band: At the top of the hoof, just below the hairline, is a soft part of the hoof wall which is rich in blood vessels. Hoof growth originates at the coronary band. It is thought that irritating the coronary band with chemicals will increase the rate of hoof growth. Exercise stimulates the coronary band, and an unbalanced hoof, taking more impact on one side than the other, will stimulate the coronary band to grow hoof faster on the stressed side. The coronary band "thinks" that the stressed side is wearing away and sends more foot to that area. If the horse is shod, the problem gets worse and worse.

Corrective Shoeing: Early in life, when the horse's bones are "plastic", corrective shoeing can sometimes help straighten out conformational defects. Later on, though, corrective shoeing more often causes more problems than it corrects.

Corticosteroid: By definition, a steroid produced by the adrenal cortex: In practice, a coverup drug inject into joints, tendons, and other parts of the horse to "normalize" him for a race or other athletic event. Corticosteroids do more damage than they prevent, inhibiting healing and covering up injuries that are then exacerbated by further participation in the sport at a time of injury. Very popular, but very stupid.

Counterirritant: Caustic chemicals injected or rubbed on, or the burning or freezing of flesh - all in order to cause an inflammatory reaction. Called "fighting fire with fire", this technique is considered barbaric and recent science tends to show that it causes more problems rather than helping heal an injury.

Creatine Phosphate Energy System: Creatine Phosphate is an extremely fast-acting muscle fuel stored within muscle cells that is used in the beginning of a race. The CP system can contribute to muscle firepower for as long as 30 seconds in very well trained athletes, or for as short a period as 5 seconds in poorly trained individuals. The CP system is nicknamed "free speed" because it does not produce fatiguing lactic acid when the athlete is working "all-out".

Creatine Phosphokinase (CPK): A muscle enzyme that appears in the blood after a hard exercise or tying up destroys muscle tissue. CPK is the most volatile of the muscle enzymes, rising rapidly after damage, then dropping quickly as repair is accomplished.

Cryotherapy: Cold treatment. The best first aid for almost all injuries. A good preventitive for some forms of lower leg filling. A painkiller.

Curb: Inflammation and thickening of the plantar ligament behind the hock.

Deconditioning: A loss of competitive fitness due to lack of appropriate exercise.

Debridement: Cutting away of tissue that is interfering with healing.

Degeneration: Deterioration of tissues.

Diagonal Gallop: A normal gallop, as in LR, RR, LF, RF.

Diagnosis: Determining precisely what is wrong, including the cause of the problem.

Diastole: The period of the cardiac cycle where the ventricles are not contracting.

Diastolic Pressure: The minimum blood pressure during the cardiac cycle - the pressure just prior to ventricular ejection.

Distal: Farthest from the center.

Diuretic: A substance that causes an increase in the volume of urine excreted.

Dorsiflexion: Bending toward the rear. In the horse, fatigue allows fetlocks to droop, overdorsiflexing them and the knees, resulting in a variety of injuries. (See overdorsiflexion.)

Drug: Any substance taken internally that alters one or more bodily functions.

Edema: Swelling.

Efficiency Score: Feet per beat. Determined by the equation: Distance/time/heartrate * 60. If a horse travels 660 feet (1/8 of a mile) in 22 seconds, at a heartrate of 165, his efficiency score is 10.91 ft/bt (660/22/165*60). We've measured efficiency scores as low as 6 ft/bt and as high as 14 ft/bt. Measurements are innaccurate at heartrates over 180 because of the anaerobic contribution to the effort. What we think we're measuring here is the overall efficiency of the animal's cardiovascular and biomechanical systems. In a laboratory setting, much more sophisticated measurements can be made, but this system seems to be quite accurate in the field and anybody with a heartrate monitor can use it. It's an easy way to compare horses without having to get them all performing at the same speeds or heartrates.

Elasticity: The ability to stretch and bend - and return to the original shape.

Electrocardiogram: (ECG, EKG) A recording of the electrical currents generated by action potentials of cardiac muscle cells.

Electrolyte: Solution that conducts electricity. In the horse, electrolyte solutions are salts (mineral ions) that the body uses during hard work and sweating. A normal diet will supply all the electrolytes your horse needs.

Electromyography (EMG): Electronic monitoring of muscle contractions triggered by an elitrical stimulous.

Electrostimulation: In cases where muscle atrophy is occuring because of an injury, electrical stimulation of muscles keeps them healthy while repair is taking place.

Endurance: The ability to handle prolongued exercise. This is a factor of fuel availability and cardiovascular efficiency.

Energy: The ability to perform work.

Enzyme: A protein that accelerates specific chemical reactions but does not undergo any change during the reaction. During a race, horses will burn fuel anaerobically, without oxygen, making use of glycolytic enzymes.

Epiphysis: Growth plates at the ends of long bones - cartilage turning to bone. With too fast growth, or too much exercise too soon, this cartilage will become inflamed (epiphysitis) and parts of it will be delayed in the changeover to bone. As a result, small pockets of cartilage will become surrounded by bone (osteochondrosis), forming a weak point that is liable to fracture later on.

Equine Gymnasium: A facility modeled upon Olympic training camps, where a variety of performance types come together to enjoy a wide range of exercise modalities supported by a strong scientific presence. None exist today.

Equitrack: This is an innovative racing surface that was proven safer and faster at Remington Park in Oklahoma City, Oklahoma, but taken out after a few years of trial. Reason? Hard to figure. Some said it was taken out because the surface became too oily in hot temperatures. Others said that big trainers shipping in to steal the big purses got disgruntled because their animals were unable to keep up with home-track runners. This would occur because foreign horses would not have had the chance to develop the neuromuscular coordination necessary to deliver the stride rate that would make them competitive at these exceptional rates of speed. Cheap horses were hitting 1:09s at Remington.

Essential Amino Acids: Amino acids that cannot be formed by the body at a rate adequate to meet metabolic requirements and must be obtained from the diet.

Etiology: The science of causes of disease or injury. This science is ignored completely at the racetrack. Trainers injure horses over and over again, doing the same stupid things, because nobody investigates the etiology of the injury.

Ethics: A rare commodity in most horsey pasttimes.

Examination: *Adams' Lameness in Horses* goes deeply into physical examination techniques for diagnosis.

Exertional Myopathy: This term refers to tying up as it applies to a horse that experiences muscle cramping at the beginning of exercise. While we tend to think of it as all types of muscle cramping, veterinarians consider tying up to occur after a long slow exercise due to muscle fuel depletion. In either case, "myopathy", or muscle cell damage, is present.

Extensor Muscle: A muscle that straightens a joint; a flexor muscle bends a joint.

Fascia: A collagen-based tissue that encases muscles and some organs. The thickening and toughening of muscle fascia parallels the development of the collagen in tendons and ligaments. A horse with hard shoulders has hard tendons.

Fast Twitch Muscle Cells: Fast contracting muscle cells preferentialy recruited for high speed or high intensity work. Also know as Type II muscle cells, and divided into two generalized groups: Type IIA muscle cells have some oxidative capacity due to the presence of mitochondria, while Type IIB muscle cells operate almost entirely anaerobically, throwing off large quantities of lactic acid as a biproduct of fuel burning. Type I cells, or Slow Twitch, are almost exclusively oxidative fuel burners, but contract slowly and are used for light, slow work. The most useful cell for the Thoroughbred racehorse is Type IIA, while endurance horses will rely on Type I muscle cells.

Feedback: The Central Nervous System is constantly receiving messages from proprioreceptors throughout the body. Thus, all the organs of the body are constantly negotiating for favorable treatment, tendons hollering "ouch!" and muscles complaining "Hey, we're drowning in lactic acid down here - ease up a little!". This kind of negative feedback interferes with performance, making a fast horse slow down.

Fibrillation: An extremely rapid contraction of cardiac muscle in an unsynchronized, repetitive way that prevents effective pumping of blood.

Fibrinogen: Blood Plasma protein that is converted into clots.

Firing: Burning, through heat or severe cold, holes in the skin over an injured part.

Foot Protractor: A device for measuring hoof angle.

GH: Growth Hormone. One of the steroids given to horses to promote growth and muscle building.

Glue-on Shoes: A great idea - if only they'd stay on. Advantages: reduced concussion, no nail holes in the hoof wall, easily replaced. Disadvantages: expensive, fall off.

Gluteus Medius Muscle: The ideal muscle to take muscle biopsies from - one of the primary propulsive muscles. Located just forward of the tail on either side of the backbone - the "bump" of the rump.

Glycogen: The body's primary fuel, derived from carbohydrates. Glycogen depletion in muscle cells can lead to one form of fatigue. Even endurance horses must have an adequate supply of glycogen because other sources of fuel, fats and proteins, burn "on the flame of glycogen". When glycogen is gone, the body dies.

Glycolysis: The breakdown of glycogen into two molecules of lactic acid - performed without oxygen.

Golgi Tendon Organs: Receptors of afferent nerve fibers wrapped around collagen bundles in tendons - activated when tendons are stretched. These sensors are meant to prevent overstretching by shutting down the actions that are causing the stretch. When you step on a rock and your ankle starts to twist, your whole leg is liable to go out from under you because the golgi tendon organs shut down the muscles of the leg to protect the tendon being stretched. If a muscular action is too strong for the tendons involved, the action will be slowed or inhibited. This is one reason for developing structural strength before attempting speed. It's also a reason not to kill pain in the lower legs - you're defeating the protective mechanisms.

Granulation Tissue: Arising from the soup of blood, necrotic tissue, debris, and the chemicals and cells of repair, granulation tissue is the first stage of repair in injuries such as wounds, bowed tendons, and muscle tears.

"Heart": The mythological attribute "class" horses exhibit in a race. Akin to courage.

Heartrate Monitor: A device that can accurately track heartrate in the freely exercising athlete. Unknown on today's racetracks, as are most sportsmedicine monitoring techniques and devices. Moronic racetrack officialdom often bans these instruments of the devil.

Heartrate Response: Whenever the body comes under stress, heartrate tends to increase in order to pump oxygen, fuels, specialized chemicals, cells and proteins, and nutrient-rich fluids to those parts of the body requiring them. Heartrate response to exercise is the most accurate non-laboratory measure of exercise intensity and relative fitness in human and equine athletes.

Heartscore: By taking an electrocardiogram and measuring the duration of the Q,R,S segment of the chart, researchers were able to achieve an accurate measurement of heart size in the horse. Modern day ultrasonography achieves a better result, but heart size has been found not to correlate well with racing performanceexcept that exceptionally large hearts tend to be found in exceptionally gifted Thoroughbreds.

Heel Cracks: "Scratches". A chafing behind the pastern that causes the skin to harden and crack. Treated with furasin ointment and possibly an antifungal.

Hematoma: A collection of blood under the skin due to bruising.

Hemoglobin: The red in red blood cells - the oxygen carrying component.

Hemoglobinuria: Hemoglobin in the urine. Black water. This is a bad sign after tying up - it means massive destruction of muscle cells has occurred and that the kidneys are under duress attempting to remove muscle debris from the blood. Kidney failure can result.

Hemorrhage: Discharge of blood. The degree of hemorrhage in a bowed tendon plays a role in how long it takes for the tendon to heal.

Hike: At the trot, the horse avoids putting weight on an injured hindlimb, causing a hike, or elevation, of the hip as the effected leg touches down.

High Speed Treadmill: As opposed to the old slow treadmills with rollers under the belt, high speed treadmills can take horses right down to racing rates on a solid, forgiving platform, and at any grade up to 10%. The perfect scientific conditioning tool.

Homeostasis: Steady State. A balance, as when the heart can pump enough blood and deliver enough oxygen to fully support the exercise load.

Horseman: A person who has shared his or her existence with horses for a long enough time that an intuitive sense of the well-being of the horse has evolved.

Hunter Reaction: If cold is applied too long, dropping the core temperatures under 20 degrees C, an autonomic reaction will open blood vessels to prevent the area from freezing. Thus, the swelling you're trying to control will be intensified. Limit icing to 15-20 minutes per application to avoid the Hunter Reaction.

Hyaluronic Acid: The viscous fluid found in synovial fluid that helps lubricate the joints. The high molecular weight of this chemical has been found to be effective in bringing injured joints back to reasonable function.

Hyperextension: When the knee of the horse bends backwards too far, then the tendons and ligaments become overstretched and tear. That's an example of a hyperextended joint.

Hyperpnea: Hyperventilation - blowing.

Hyperthermia: Excessively high body temperature.

Hypertrophy: Enlargement by way of an increase in the size of cells, as in muscle hypertrophy through conditioning.

Hypothyroidism: Horses undergoing the initial stages of training may exhibit hypothyroidism, or a deficiency in thyroxin. Symptoms: stiffness, loss of appetite, lethargic behavior, decreased endurance. T3,T4 tests will diagnose.

Hypoxia: Lack of sufficient oxygen.

Idiopathic: Of unknown cause or origin.

Immobilization: Used in cases where normal movements will cause further injury. Not a good policy in cases where exercise may accelerate healing or prevent atrophy or adhesions.

Inflammation: Heat and swelling near injured or infected tissues due to increased blood supply and chemical activity.

Infrared Thermography: Infrared light is radiated by heat. Certain cameras have been developed to "see" infrared light, thus, a thermal map of an animal, a factory roof, or the entire Earth, can be thrown onto a computer screen for examination. In horses, thermography warns of oncoming injury by detecting inflammatory processes before clinical signs of lameness are present.

Injury: Any disruption of normal bodily tissues not due to disease or parasites.

Intervention: Catching an oncoming injury early, before it becomes a major problem, then acting to eliminate the cause while allowing and encouraging complete repair.

Initial Stabilization Phase: At the onset of high intensity exercise, the autonomic nervous system triggers a rapid increase in heartrate that sometimes overshoots demand. At a certain point, though, due to feedback systems that are constantly monitoring body conditions, heartrate is stabilized, and responds to exercise demands in a more controlled way. The fitter the athlete becomes, the less error in attenuating heartrate to actual exercise demand.

Innervation: Nerve stimulation of a muscle.

Interosseous Membrane/Ligament: Connective tissue membrane between bones, as between the splint bones and the cannon bones in horses.

Interval Training: A training method consisting of multiple bouts of exercise separated by partial recovery rest periods. The technique allows a larger volume of higher intensity exercise to performed in a workout without risk of fatigue and injury.

Intra-articular: In the joint.

Intrafibrillar covalent crosslinks: Collagen fibers are crosslinked in the mature tendon. With a tendon rupture, these crosslinks are destroyed or distorted and the collagen that develops during the repair process very slowly achieves maturity, with these crosslinks finally redeveloping.

Ipsilateral: On the same side - left fore and left hind are ipsilateral legs.

Ischemia: Lack of blood to an area - bandages can cause ischemia in the superficial flexor tendon and lead to a bow.

Jacks: Cunean tendinitis.

Joint Capsule: Fibrous enclosure around synovial joint.

Ketones (Ketone Bodies): Products of fatty acid oxidation that accumulate in the blood after a period of starvation. Ketones inhibit glycogen burning - the body is triggered to save fuel. Latest science says that feeding 1/3 cup of corn oil over each feeding will reduce blood ketones to zero - allowing muscle cells to burn a higher percentage of their stored fuel. This means the horse can maintain speed longer.

Krebs Cycle: The oxidative pathway for the burning of carbohydrates, proteins, and fat. Takes place in highly oxidative muscle cells - mostly Slow Twitch.

LSD (Long Slow Distance): Long Slow distance refers to the initial stage of training, where background mileage is built gradually, with slow work going longer and longer day by day. This is called the LSD stage.

LTLH (Long Toe Low Heel): Many racehorses are shod with underslung heels, low hoof angles, and long toes. This is the perfect shoeing configuration to produce fatigue and bowed tendons.

Lactic Acid: A weak acid formed during the incomplete anaerobic burning of glycogen within muscle cells. Lactic acid is also formed in the equine gut in the digestion of carbohydrates. Lactic acid is at once, the principal cause of fatigue in hard-working athletes, and the principal source of fuel in athletes trained to the extent that they have developed a higher percentage of Fast Twitch High Oxidative (Type IIA) muscle cells.

Lactic Dehydrogenase(LDH): A muscle enzyme with 5 isoenzymes that, through analysis of blood, can tell you if there has been muscle damage and, if so, weather that muscle was the heart or skeletal muscle.

Ladder Workouts: A succession of heats of speed at increasing or decreasing distances. Human athletes will take ladder workouts up in distance and then down. With horses, we tend to play it safe and use only down ladders, as in successive heats of 1 mile, 3/4, and 5/8ths. Ladder workouts are good for variety and good for maintaining a racing horse. They're not as specific, though, as straight intervals. If you're looking to develop speed, for example, a 6 X 1/2 workout is far more specific for that need than a ladder workout that contains longer and slower heats. Stanerra won the Japan Cup coming off ladder workouts.

Lameness: An injury with observable negative effects on gait and performance. A horse can be injured without becoming lame.

Lameness Intervention: Detect oncoming injury, completely diagnose, eliminate the cause(s), carefully reintroduce workload.

Laminitis: An inflammation of the laminae of the foot that often results in the separation and rotation downward of the coffin bone(founder).

Latent Period: The period between the initiation of an action potential in a muscle fiber and the beginning of mechanical work. EMG (electromyographic) machines can measure the quickness of a muscle group in a horse, non-invasively, and give you a relative firepower index of that animal's propulsive muscles. A lot of this kind of research was done on horses at Texas A&M, but the researcher went back to Japan and the project, I believe, has died. Should be started again.

Latent Phase: A delay in heartrate response to the onset of high intensity exercise. The better conditioned the athlete, the shorter the latent phase of heartrate response.

Learning: The increase in the likelihood of a particular response to a stimulus as a consequence of experience. When muscle cells are exposed to high demands, they "learn" to deal with the stresses of those demands - lactic acid, fuel depletion, etc. Most of the organs of living things "learn" in this context.

Linear Relationship: As A increases, B increases in equal proportion. On a graph, this type of dependent relationship produces a straight line. In a race, lactic acid production begins as a linear response to speed, but, once the horse crosses his anaerobic threshold, lactate production increases geometrically - in an upward-sweeping curve. What this means is that, at the end of a race, lactic acid comes on like gangbusters, and the horse either has to be able to deal with it, or he stops or breaks down.

Macrocycle: A conditioning cycle that runs from season to season, lasting 6 months to a year. These are strategic rebuilding cycles meant to improve the athlete's overall capacity for work. Structural and tissue adaptations occur, and the cycle takes the athlete through competition. Within macrocycles are microcycles and mesocycles (see below).

Maximum Heartrate: Every individual, human or equine, has a maximum heartrate, and with age, that maximum possible heartrate slowly declines. It's a good sign for an athlete to be able to rev up his heart to high numbers on demand, but not so hot to show high heartrates for a given piece of submaximal work. In horses, the highest heartrates measured, that were not considered fibrillation, were in the 240 range. Peak heartrates during Thoroughbred races range from 216 to 225 - these are not maximum heartrates, just high percentages of the animals' actual maximum heartrate.

Mechanoreceptor: A sensory receptor that responds preferentially to mechanical stimuli, such as bending, twisting, or compressing.

Mesocycle: A conditioning cycle usually lasting two or three months. During such a cycle, the athlete is brought to a new level of fitness and performance.

Metabolism: All the chemical reactions that occur within a living organism.

Microcycle: A short cycle of work and recovery, lasting ten days to two weeks. Conditioning performed during a microcycle is of a tactical nature, as in setting a horse up for an individual race.

Microtrauma: Microscopic lesion or injury. Virtually all hard exercise causes microtrauma in muscles, bones, and connective tissues. Repair can take just a few hours or weeks, depending on the tissue and the severity of damage. Those tissues with good blood supply repair most quickly, unless that blood supply has been damaged.

Mitochondria: Rod-shaped living organisms within tissues that combine fuels with oxygen, providing an aerobic energy source. Site of the Krebs Cycle. Mitochondria density in muscle cells is a measure of oxidative capacity of those cells. Training can induce a population of mitochondria within Fast Twitch muscle cells, allowing for the burning of lactic acid as a primary fuel and extending the time a horse can maintain high intensity exercise.

Motor Neuron: An efferent neuron which innervates skeletal muscle fibers.

Mucous Membranes: Lining the gut, sinuses, and respiratory tract are thin tissues that produce mucous, protecting the underlying tissues. These mucous membranes are easily disturbed and can lead to signs of bleeding in racehorses. It is well known that most NSAIDs, like Bute, Banamine, and aspirin can cause mucous membrane lesions. Once formed, these lesions become sites of bleeding, infection, inflammation, swelling and pain. One researcher has discovered that ulcers among racehorses are very common and that, avoiding NSAIDS and feeding liquid Maalox will alleviate symptoms and help the healing process.

Muscle Biopsy: the taking of a sample of muscle (about the size of the last joint of your little finger) via biopsy needle. The middle gluteus muscle is the most common site. The object of a muscle biopsy is to determine the ratio of fast twitch to slow twitch cells, the mitochondria density of the muscle cells, and the fuel/enzyme content of the muscle cells.

Muscle Fiber Types: There are three principal muscle fiber types, Slow Twitch (ST or Type I), Fast Twitch (FT or Type IIB), and Fast Twitch High Oxidative (FTH or Type IIA). Slow Twitch fibers contract slowly and use oxygen in burning muscle fuels. Fast Twitch fibers contract quickly and burn glycogen enzymatically, or without the use of oxygen. Fast Twitch muscle cells throw off lactic acid as a bi-product of inefficient fuel burning, but FTH muscle cells contain mitochondria and oxidative enzymes (among them, citrate synthase) which allow them to burn lactic acid and other fuels using oxygen. Essentially, the more mitochondria in an FTH muscle cell, the less lactate it will throw off, and the longer it can keep on firing. We need as many FTH cells as we can get and we can change the fiber type ratios through conditioning.

Muscle Fuel: Muscles can use carbohydrates (in the form of glycogen), fats (in the form of triglycerides and free fatty acids), and proteins (in the form of amino acids) as fuel. In addition, all skeletal muscles store away Phosphocreatine (PC) as a fast-acting sprint fuel.

Muscle Enzymes: There are chemicals, enzymes, that are normally only present in muscle cells, among them CPK, SGOT, and LDH. When muscle damage occurs, these chemicals are spilled into the blood stream, and measuring their presence in the blood stream will enable you to determine the extent of muscle damage.

Muscle Hypertrophy: With exercise, muscles will grow larger, in part because they are swelling with stored fuel. But high intensity exercise will cause individual muscle cells to increase their diameters and contraction strengths while long slow exercise tends to encourage muscle fibers to split and become more numerous. Either way, overall muscle bulk tends to increase.

Myoglobin: The oxygen-carrying protein within muscles. When muscle tissue is damaged, as in tying up, myoglobin flows into the bloodstream and is eliminated in the urine. The condition is called myoglobinurea or black water.

Myositis: Muscle inflammation.

Navicular Syndrome: Any horse traveling over very hard ground or shod with underslung heels is likely to develop a foot soreness that, upon hoof testing, appears to originate at the navicular bone. Sometimes, the navicular is actually involved and deteriorating, but, more often, pinched heels and lack of circulation is causing that area of the foot to become inflamed. Eliminating pinched or underslung heels and treating with circulation enhancers can often completely cure the condition.

Necrosis: The death of tissues, leaving behind pockets of debris, catabolic enzymes, and scavenger cells that can cause further damage to nearby tissues.

Negative Feedback: A control system that inhibits an action. When Golgi Tendon organs sense that the tendon is overstretching, they inhibit the commands to the muscles that are causing the stretch.

Neural Nodes: Switches which receive a action potentials from nerves and send out chemicals that activate muscle fibers. With practice, these neurotransmitting chemicals build up around often-used nodes and the resulting actions are quicker and more powerful.

Neurectomy: Nerving. Cutting, removing, blocking or dissolving nerves that serve an injured part will allow the once-lame horse to go back to work as if nothing is wrong. Many, many racehorses have been nerved, usually the nerves serving the feet.

Nonsteroidal Anti-inflammatories (NSAIDs): Bute, Banamine, Aspirin, Ibuprofen. Not as potent a coverup as corticosteroids such as dexamethasone, but with fewer negative side-effects.

Open Knees: A dished appearance of the knees when looking at them from the side. Usually occurs in horses undergoing work or being overfed at ages 1-3. This is epiphysitis. Has nothing to do with closure of the growth plates.

Osselets: Traumatic arthritis of the fetlock. The same condition farther down the pastern is called ringbone.

Osteoarthritis: Chronic joint disease of joints including the destruction of cartilage and a bony overgrowth.

Osteoblasts: Cells that lay down bone.

Osteochondrosis Dissecans: Cartilage disease where a piece of cartilage has broken away - as in knee and ankle "chips".

Overdorsiflexion: Bending backward too far. With fatigue, poor conformation, or incorrect shoeing, the fetlock and the knee of the horse will overdorsiflex, putting excess strain on all the parts of the suspension system as well as upon the bones and cartilage of the knee and ankle joints.

Overtraining: Bringing on workloads that are too severe for the athlete's current state of readiness. Acute overtraining produces injuries. Chronic overtraining eventually produces injuries, too, but the real problem is a general debilitation in both performance capabilities and physical health. Chronic overtraining, depending on how long overtraining has been going on, can require a long rebuilding.

Oxyhemoglobin: Hemoglobin combined with oxygen.

Palpation: Feeling for an injury with the fingers.

Palpitation: A rapid beating of the heart.

Paratendon: The sheath of tissue that surrounds tendons, providing a blood supply and protection. With injury to the tendon, the paratenon is liable to develop adhesions with the tendon, limiting the flexibility and stretching capacity of the tendon. These adhesions often break, causing swelling that can look like a bow. Keeping the horse moving, and avoiding stupidities like firing, will help to avoid adhesions.

Patella: Knee cap, located in the stifle joint.

Pericardium: Fascia bag surrounding the heart.

pH: The negative logarithm to the base 10 of the hydrogen ion concentration. A measure of acidity. The pH decreases as the acidity increases.

Pharmacology: The most important applied science in today's performance horse scene: drugs.

Physical Therapy: An active healing mode using exercise, cryotherapy, heat, massage, electrotherapy, ultrasound, lasers, and other techniques. Can be quite effective in accelerating rehabilitation.

Plasma: The liquid portion of blood. In a laboratory, whole blood is placed in a centrifuge where solids are collected at the bottom of the tube. The liquid portion, the plasma, is then poured off and used for testing and analysis.

Plasticity: The capacity of tissues to change their structure and composition in response to stimuli. Bone, muscle fibers, nerve tissue - almost all the tissues of the body are "plastic".

Positive Dissociation: In a trot or a pace, where the rear foot impacts slightly before the front foot. This kind of stride is more energy efficient and can be encouraged through shoeing - front angles higher than "normal"; rear angles lower than normal. First mentioned by Professor George Pratt in one of his scientific papers.

Posterior: Toward the rear.

Poultice: A topical mixture that will draw fluids from the tissues it comes in contact with.

Prognosis: Prediction of the eventual results of a disease or injury. Most prognoses of racehorse injuries are overly optimistic.

Progressive Loading: An exercise protocol that brings on the workload gradually, step by step, and continuously - flattening out the workload' ends most of the conditioning response. In other words, if you're doing the same thing today that you were doing last week, you're going nowhere. Conversely, if you jump from slow work to high speed work suddenly, structural systems are bound to fail.

Pro-oxidants: Chemicals such as Iron, Ozone, and Polyunsaturated Fats, encourage the formation of free radicals and the destruction of cells. Oxidative stress can be encountered after hard work, disease, or injury. See "antioxidants".

Prophylaxis: Guarding against injury or disease - nearly unknown science in performance horsing.

Proprioreceptors: Nerve endings that pick up messages from peripheral body parts and send them back to the Central Nervous System. These messages can trigger hormone production, changes in blood chemistry, reflex actions, or inhibit muscles from firing at full power.

Prostaglandin: A fatty acid responsible for vasodilatation and swelling - aspirin and bute inhibit its actions.

Protocol: A system. A way of doing things. Most scientific protocols are step by step procedures designed to produce a given effect or event. This in contrast to a "Hmm, what would it be fun to do today?" training gameplan.

Proximal: Close to a given point. As in, the bit should be placed proximal to the head.

Psychosomatic: Physical disorder caused by the mind. We give our horses too much credit for mental powers in this area. If you look hard enough you will find that they're really hurt.

Pulsating Electromagnetic Field Therapy (PEMF): The "blue boot" made this therapy famous. No miracles here, though.

QRS: The component of the electrocardiogram corresponding to the depolarization of the ventricles. A long QRS duration indicates a large heart.

Quarter Crack: Split hoof behind the curve of the hoof. Generally due to improper shoeing - fitting a shoe too small, nailing behind the curve.

Quittor: Nasty infection/necrosis of a ligament in the foot.

Radiation Safety: Not practiced at the racetrack. X-ray radiation is sprayed every which way as trainers grow impatient and veterinarians hurry.

Recovery Cycle: The process of stress, recovery, rebound. This includes tissue repair, refueling, enzyme recovery. Normal recovery cycles from a race last about 48 to 72 hours.

Recovery Heartrate: When exercise stops, the heartrate drops quickly, but may take 30 minutes or more to reach the resting rate that the horse showed before the saddle was put on. But at the end of the initial rapid drop in heartrate, there is a plateau that occurs between one minute and 90 seconds after cessation of the exercise. This is the "recovery heartrate" we use in training horses for high intensity events because it lets us know how much lactic acid is being produced from heat to heat in an interval workout. The heartrate will continue to drop, slowly, but this plateau is the important number for assessing the athlete's proximity to fatigue.

Red Blood Cells: Platelets containing hemoglobin that transport oxygen to bodily organs. Some 30-50% are stored away in the spleen and can become spiculated (hard and wrinkled) if they remain in the spleen too long.

Red Muscle Fibers: Slow Twitch muscle cells.

Regeneration: Growth or repair of damaged or stressed tissues.

Repetition Workouts: These are multiple-heat workouts with full recovery rest periods between, meant to develop speed as opposed to stamina. Interval workouts are more directed toward high-speed stamina.

Resistance Exercise: Uphill gallops, running on treadmills at a grade, pulling braked Standardbred bikes - all these are examples of resistance exercise. Horses can build sprinting power while working at slower, less concussive, rates. Human athletes are now running against parachutes.

Resorption: When bone isn't being used as hard as before, mineral resorption occurs and the bone becomes less dense.

Respiratory Rate: The rate of breathing is governed by oxygen debt (lactic acidosis) or heat buildup - but at a gallop, respiration takes place in sync with the stride.

Resting Heartrate: Heartrate taken in the stall in the morning before the hustle and bustle of the stable begins. Resting heartrates typically range from 33 to 43 beats per minute, but have been recorded as low as 19 BPM. An elevated resting heartrate in a horse that is monitored daily can suggest discomfort due to disease or injury, making timely intervention possible.

Ringbone: Osteoarthritis of the pastern.

Rotary Gallop: The galloping stride revolves around the body, as in LR, RR, RF, LF. This stride produces more acceleration, is costly in energy output, and can lead to interference and injury. Proper shoeing can help alleviate the negative aspects of this stride.

SAID Principle: Specific Adaptation to Imposed Demands. This is the entire basis for exercise in the athlete. See Specificity.

SGOT: A muscle enzyme that spills into the blood stream when muscle cells have been damaged. Blood tests measuring SGOT and two other muscle enzymes, LDH and CPK, can let you know if the soreness your horse is experiencing is due to muscle damage or another cause. SGOT peaks later than CPK and elevations last longer after muscle damage - as in tying up. Muscle soreness onset can be delayed for a few days after a hard workout, so SGOT is sometimes a better indicator of damage that occurred earlier.

Serotonin: A neurotransmitting hormone.

Skeletal Muscle Pump: The pumping effect of contracting muscles on the bloodflow around them. After hard exercise, a warmdown period of moderate exercise allows the skeletal muscle pump to rid the muscles of waste products and debris. The same is true for exercise in succeeding days after a hard race. Walking doesn't do much pumping.

Slow Twitch Muscle Cells: Highly oxidative, slow contracting muscle cells accounting for about 1/3 of the skeletal muscle in most horses. these cells are preferentially recruited for slow or light work and produce very little, if any, lactic acid. These cells will burn a lot of the lactic acid produced during high intensity exercise if slow exercise is continued for ten or more minutes after the hard exercise has ceased.

Specificity of Exercise: Effective exercise mimics the actual event the athlete is training for. Non-specific exercise is a waste of time, except when building a base of Long Slow Distance that will enable the performance of a larger volume of event-specific exercise later on.

Speed Bias: A term describing certain racetrack conditions. In Thoroughbred racing, horses often have a lot of speed and no staying power. These animals are almost invariably raced the wrong way - running them as fast as they'll go until they stop from exhaustion. Once in a while, racetrack officials, who may or may not have a vested interest in doing so, tighten down the racetrack surface by working it over and over again, reducing its depth and making the surface harder. This makes for a faster, less fatiguing racing surface, giving "speed" horses two advantages. Their fast stride turnover can be used more effectively on such a surface while slower-strided horses cannot keep up. That extra speed is less costly to the sprinter because he's not moving an extra 10 pounds of dirt with every stride, so fatigue is automatically delayed. In general, a track set up with a speed bias is a safer track to run over for all horses, but a sudden change in racing surface toward one with higher concussive forces violates the "no surprises" rule for structural soundness. Racetracks should endeavor to provide the fastest surface possible every day.

Splint: Between the splint bone and the cannon bone is an interosseus ligament that attaches one to the other. Fine filaments from the ligament penetrate each bone. When stress on the cannon bone is rapidly increased, remodeling begins, and, during the remodeling, the cannon bone becomes more porous. When that happens, the filaments pull out of the cannon bone and the splint bone comes loose. Then all hell breaks loose as the body tries to fasten the splint securely in place. A bump of new bone growth forms and the whole area becomes inflamed and sore. If the area of activity is near the suspensory ligament, then the healing process turns into an injury process for the suspensory as the new bone rubs against it.

Sportsmedicine: An umbrella word that covers all the scientific disciplines as they apply to sport. These can include biomechanics, nutrition, exercise physiology, clinical medicine, biochemistry, ergonomics, physics, surgery - you name it. It all boils down to applied science to preserve and enhance athletic capabilities.

Steady State: A level of exertion where oxygen delivery and oxygen demand are in equilibrium. If the horse continues at this level of work, the heartrate will not increase over an extended period of time, but if the horse works just a little harder, the heartrate will steadily increase even if the speed does not. In other words, a horse traveling at 10 meters per second and maintaining a steady 170 heartrate is at his steady state if increasing his speed to 10.1 meters per second causes his heartrate to climb and keep climbing. Steady state is usually a level of exertion lower than that represented by VLA4 - the anaerobic threshold.

Stress: Any environmental change that must be adapted to if health and life are to be maintained - or if athletic performance is to be enhanced.

Stressor: Anything that upsets the body's chemical or structural balances.

Synovitis: Inflammation of the synovial membrane.

Systole: The period when the ventricles of the heart are contracting.

Tendinitis: Inflammation of a tendon and/or tendon sheath.

Tendon: A bundle of collagen fibers that connects muscle to bone and transmits the contractile force of the muscle to the bone.

Torsion: Twisting.

Trauma: Wound or injury.

Trigger Phase: That brief period of time where heartrate is shooting up in response to the onset of hard exercise. Trigger Phase ends at the Initial Stabilization Phase.

V160: The velocity, measured in meters per second, at which the athlete develops a heartrate of 160 BPM.

V200: The velocity at which the athlete develops a heartrate of 200 BPM.

VLA4: The velocity at which plasma lactic acid reaches 4 millimoles per liter. The equivalent of the anaerobic threshold.

VO2MAX: The velocity at which maximum oxygen uptake is reached.

Vasoconstriction: Decrease in the diameter of a blood vessel.

Vasodilatation: Increase in the diameter of a blood vessel.

Vein: A wide, thin-walled vessel that carries blood back to the heart.

Viscoelastic: Having both viscous and elastic properties - as with cartilage.

Viscosity: Resistance to flow. Hyaluronic Acid is a viscous liquid.

Work: Force times distance. W=FX. The physical displacement of matter.

XYV Ligaments (Sometimes called "XYZ" ligaments on the racetrack): Leading down behind the pastern, these consist of: 1) X, the deep distal sesamoidian ligament; 2) Y, the superficial (straight) distal sesamoidian ligament; and, 3) V, the middle (oblique) distal sesamoidian ligament. These ligaments, along with the superficial and deep flexor tendons, are part of the stay apparatus of the leg.

INDEX

sesamoiditis, 17
sheath: tendon, 98
shoeing: long toes, 28, 35,
   147, 150-153, 167;
   low heels, 28, 147, 150-
   152, 167;
   rims, 149;
   rockered toes, 148;
   rolled toes, 148;
   swedges, 149;
   toe grabs, 21, 35, 41, 46,
   146, 147, 149, 167;
   toe lengths, 38, 149, 151;
   trailers, 146;
   underslung heels, 35, 36,
   38, 124, 150-153
Silver, Dr. Ian, 95
SOD, 100, 126, 127, 129
sodium bicarbonate, 119, 120
specificity of exercise, 117
splint bones, 17, 146
stay apparatus, 17
stocking up, 27, 28, 160, 161
stress, 24, 28, 31, 33, 42-46,
   57, 63, 66-68, 76, 80, 89,
   96, 97, 101, 107, 108, 113,
   114, 126-129, 135, 138,
   145, 161
stretch, 14, 15, 17, 24, 32, 57,
   67, 68, 108, 117, 119, 137,
   146
stretch: homestretch, 117
supercompensation, 125
superoxide, 100, 126, 127
suspensory, 161
swelling, 21, 23-25, 27-29, 45,
   55-57, 60, 64, 65, 71-78,
   80-83, 85, 86, 91-93, 96,
   98, 99, 107, 108, 128, 159,
   160-164
synovial fluid, 128, 129, 180
tendinitis, 17, 29, 32, 39, 44,
   117, 147, 157, 159

tendon: deep digital flexor, 25,
   27, 32, 45, 55-58, 60, 79,
   145, 146, 161, 163
tendon splitting, 95, 96
tenosynovitis, 17
therapy: antioxidant, 100;
   electromagnetic, 102;
   icing, 34, 71, 74, 76, 78,
   105, 106,;
   ultrasound, 78
thermography, 58, 164
thermometer: infrared, 164
tie up, 75
trainers, 23, 25, 39, 41, 44,
   48, 50-52, 57, 96, 117, 121,
   143, 148
tranquilizer, 75, 76, 107, 109
trotters, 42, 142
ultrasound: diagnostic, 76;
   scanning, 29, 56, 64, 71,
   72, 75, 76, 81, 105, 106;
   therapeutic - see therapy,
   ultrasound
veterinarian, 67, 71, 75, 85,
   86, 88, 100
Vetrap, 158
Vitaflex, 100, 128
vitamins, 100, 126-129
warmdown, 155, 156
warmup, 105, 124, 133, 155,
   167
windpuffs, 87
Winstrol V, 102
wraps, 22, 28, 41, 45, 73, 78,
   80-83, 98, 106, 157-161
X-ray, 165